The Great Popular Standards Songbook

Arranged and Edited by Dan Fox

CARL FISCHER®

62 Cooper Square, New York, NY 10003

ATF127

ISBN 0-8258-2585-7

Contents

Foreword

As the 21st century dawns, American songs dominate the world's popular music. Whether you're on the streets of Cairo, in the night clubs of Buenos Aires, the pubs of London, the hotels of Tokyo, or the cabarets of Hong Kong, most of what you hear is of American origin. Although this seems natural to us today, at the turn of the previous century it would have seemed most unlikely. At that time American popular song was in its formative stage. Like America itself, early popular song was a melting pot of influences from the minstrel show, vaudeville, Broadway, European opera and operetta, Jewish klezmer music, and especially from African-American composers and performers who gave us ragtime, the blues, and jazz.

The minstrel show was one of the chief forms of entertainment during the nineteenth century. Minstrelsy started in the late 1820's with a few performers in blackface strutting around the stage, singing, dancing, playing the banjo and other instruments, and telling rough jokes to the unsophisticated audiences of the day. By the last decades of the century, minstrel shows had developed into huge extravaganzas with dozens of performers and large orchestras. In those less sensitive times no one thought twice about performing in blackface. Indeed, the concept of performing with face darkened by burnt cork remained important well into the 1930s Among the hundreds of performers who used blackface in their acts, the names of Al Jolson and Eddie Cantor stand out. Even some African-American players (whom managers decided were not quite dark enough) used blackface to "enhance" their acts. Minstrelsy gave us many memorable songs, including "Dixie" and "Carry Me Back to Old Virginny," but since this book is primarily about the twentieth century, most of the songs are drawn from the world of vaudeville, itself heavily influenced by the minstrel show.

Many of our era's most popular entertainers got their start in vaudeville. In comedy we had Jack Benny, Fred Allen, Bert Williams, Burns and Allen, W.C.Fields, Buster Keaton, Bob Hope and the Marx Brothers to name just a few. Fred and Adele Astaire and Buck and Bubbles perfected their dance routines there. The great singers included Al Jolson, Fanny Brice, Ted Lewis, Sophie Tucker, and Nora Bayes. Many of the songs associated with them are still played and sung, and you'll find a dozen of the best of them in this book.

The name vaudeville comes from the French "Vau-de-Vire," a valley in Normandy through which the river Vire flows. This district is noted for its light, convivial songs, and by the early years of the 19th century, the name had come to mean any light entertainment. In many ways vaudeville was similar to minstrelsy except for the blackface, but as we have seen with the careers of Al Jolson and Eddie Cantor, even this distinction was often blurred. By the 1890s vaudeville had spread from its beginnings in the New York metropolitan area to a network of theaters all over the country, and in 1913 its premier theater, the Palace, opened in New York. Vaudeville was by far the most popular form of entertainment in a country that had yet to discover movies, radio, or television. For as little as twenty-five cents you got as many as nine different acts, everything from trained dogs, jugglers, dancers and acrobats to serious short stage works, comedians and singers. And, unlike burlesque, vaudeville was designed as family entertainment which meant a larger and more loyal audience.

As a medium for presenting new songs to the public, vaudeville was unexcelled. Early on, singers discovered the power of audience participation, and many a song became a hit because of a catchy singalong chorus. Among many others, you'll find such great standards as "April Showers," "By the Light of the Silvery Moon," and "Moonlight Bay" in this book. Other songs were written for a particular performer, or even by the performers themselves. Nora Bayes, one of the many Jewish-American stars of vaudeville (Her real name was Dora Goldberg), wrote "Shine On, Harvest Moon" with her second husband, Jack Norworth. The song lasted a lot longer than their marriage, and Bayes performed it throughout her long career.

Fanny Brice (nee Fannie Borach) was another Jewish-American star of vaudeville who also went on to great successes in Broadway musicals and as "Baby Snooks" on the radio. Equally at home with comedy or dramatic songs, she was a trailblazer

for later female comedy and singing stars such as Bette Midler, Carol Burnett and Barbra Streisand who portrayed Brice in two film biographies "Funny Girl" and "Funny Lady." Brice started her career in burlesque, an offshoot of vaudeville that featured scantily dressed chorus girls, strippers, and baggy pants comedians doing "blue" (sexually suggestive) material. Routines that depended, for example, on the slightly suggestive sound of the word "scrutinize" seem quaintly naive by today's standards, but were racy enough in earlier days to have burlesque completely banned in New York City (of all places) in 1936. The burlesque houses promptly moved across the Hudson River to Union City, New Jersey where they flourished for many more years. As crude as burlesque was, it was a training ground for many who later became stars in other venues including Abbott and Costello, Phil Silvers, and of course Gypsy Rose Lee, beguiling subject of the musical "Gypsy." This book features three songs associated with Fanny Brice's career, "Rose of Washington Square," "For Me and My Gal," and the hilarious "Second Hand Rose."

Probably the greatest star that vaudeville ever saw was Russian-born Asa Yoelson, better known as Al Jolson. Although he never played the Palace, Jolson's career spanned over 40 years, always as the star of the show. His first break was in blackface in a 1909 minstrel show, and soon his cocky "You ain't heard nothin' yet!" was heard in dozens of musical shows, especially on the stage of New York's Winter Garden Theater, as well as radio and the movies. In the 1940s his colorful life was the subject of two film biographies "The Jolson Story" and "Jolson Sings Again." Many of the songs that he introduced have remained staples of singers' repertoires. These include "My Mammy," "Rock-a-Bye Your Baby (With a Dixie Melody)," "You Made Me Love You," and George Gershwin's first big hit "Swanee," all in this book.

With the advent of radio and, later, television the golden age of this form of entertainment ended in the 1930s. But the spirit of vaudeville lives on, and in some big cities you can still find clubs and theaters that feature vaudeville and burlesque acts.

Theater existed in North America even before there was a United States, but musical theater as we know it is only about a hundred years old. Its roots include European opera and operettas, but the modern American musical may be said to begin with the formidable figure of George M. Cohan. This Irish-American genius of the stage seems to have been the first to present a coherent story in which the songs are integrated into the plot. His 1901 "Little Johnny Jones" gave us "The Yankee Doodle Boy," better known as "I'm a Yankee Doodle Dandy," and subsequent shows presented enduring favorites like "Give My Regards to Broadway," and "You're a Grand Old Flag."

Jerome Kern is one of our most beloved popular composers. He is often given credit for bridging the gap between operetta and a grander style of American musical theater epitomized by his 1927 masterpiece "Showboat" which at this writing is finishing up yet another hugely successful run on Broadway. Kern is represented in this book by some earlier songs, his personal favorite and title of his film biography "Till the Clouds Roll By," the inspirational "Look for the Silver Lining," and the remarkably modern-sounding "They Didn't Believe Me," which dates from 1914 but sounds as though it was written 30 years later.

When asked what place Irving Berlin had in American music, Kern remarked, "Berlin has no *place* in American music; He *is* American music. Né Isidor Baline in Russia, Berlin emigrated as a young boy and soon became as American as apple pie. His contributions to popular music would fill a book by themselves, but we've chosen a few early gems to represent his work. The song that made him famous was written for a Friar's Club evening in 1911. Inspired by a character in a vaudeville sketch by McIntyre and Heath, "Alexander's Ragtime Band" became Berlin's first international hit. (As has often been noted, this is a song about ragtime, not a ragtime song.) Berlin wrote songs in every popular style, and at least 150 are considered enduring standards. This from a man who could not read or write music, and who had to play on a specially built piano equipped with a lever which transposed his music to other keys from the only key in which he could play, G-flat major! "A Pretty Girl is Like a Melody" epitomizes the big production number. "All By Myself" shows Berlin at his intimate, plaintive best.

Included in this collection are many other great songs written for the Broadway stage, among them "Alice Blue Gown," "Poor Butterfly," "Pretty

Baby," and "I'm Just Wild About Harry." This last song comes from an all-Black 1921 musical called "Shuffle Along," written by Noble Sissle and the indomitable Eubie Blake. (On the occasion of his 95th birthday Eubie is quoted as saying, "If I'd known I was going to live this long I woulda taken better care of myself.") To hear about a hit all-Black musical in our day is not surprising. Think of "Ain't Misbehavin'" and "The Wiz" to name just two. But in 1921 it was still a novelty. Even more surprising, all-Black shows were known as early as 1896 when one opened successfully in New York. Because of the overwhelming dominance of African-American songwriters and performers in blues, ragtime, and jazz, the contributions of important songwriters like Blake, Shelton Brooks ("Some of These Days," "Darktown Strutters' Ball"), James Bland ("Carry Me Back to Old Virginny," "Golden Slippers" etc.) and Bob Cole ("Under the Bamboo Tree") are sometimes overlooked.

———————

Tin Pan Alley was the name given to a stretch of 28th street in New York City where many song publishers had their offices. Nowadays the music business seems to be run by lawyers and accountants with a few huge companies dominating the market, but in the 1880s and 90s there were hundreds of small independent publishers, each one striving to find that one hit that would put them on easy street. In those days almost every family had a piano, and it was not uncommon for a piece of sheet music to sell a million copies. At the standard price of 40 cents, this was a gross of $400,000, a huge fortune in the money of that era. This was a situation that attracted many entrepreneurs, few of whom were interested in music as their primary concern. For example, the Remick brothers, who started the company that would become the huge Warner Bros. conglomerate, started out with a small hand-cranked press that one of them had received as a birthday present. After trying to make a few dollars by printing announcements and flyers, they discovered that more money could be made by printing music and selling sheet music. From this unpromising start to an empire worth millions took perhaps forty years.

Songs from Tin Pan Alley are an important part of the American heritage. Many of them were written for the vaudeville stars of the day; others were turned into hits by pianists in department stores and music shops who were hired to demonstrate the songs for prospective customers. (George Gershwin started this way!) Many of the songs in this book were written in Tin Pan Alley including instrumental novelties like "12th Street Rag" and "Johnson Rag," barbershop ballads like "Ace in the Hole," "Down by the Old Mill Stream," and "I Want a Girl (Just Like the Girl that Married Dear Old Dad)," and what we'd call pop songs like "Ain't We Got Fun" and "Margie."

———————

Also included here are special categories of songs. Fans of The Three Stooges will find the tune that introduced all their movie shorts, "Listen to the Mockingbird." Listeners to PBS radio's "Prairie Home Companion" will try to fit the words that Garrison Keillor sings to its original melody, "Tishomingo Blues."

There are a half dozen great standards from the gay 90s including "A Bicycle Built for Two," "Bill Bailey," and "The Sidewalks of New York." (see "From the Turn of the Century")

The section called "Waltzes and Tearjerkers" will give you a chance to sob while you sing. Various service songs are also represented and you'll even discover that the music for the "Marines' Hymn" was written by none other than Jacques Offenbach, French composer of the (in)famous "Can-Can" from "Orpheus in the Underworld."

———————

White America didn't pay much attention to Black music until after the Civil War. One result of that terrible conflict was that the songs the Negro troops sang became known to their white officers. Soon after the War the Fisk Jubilee Singers started performing Negro spirituals, the first time that most Americans had ever heard these haunting melodies. Collections of these beautiful songs were published and enjoyed in the parlors of white and black America.

"The blues has always been," said one former slave. From its origins in the work songs and field hollers (sung *a cappella*), the blues had developed a much greater sophistication in the years following the Civil War. This was in no small part because the harmonica (renamed "blues harp") and guitar were for the first time easily available for the innovations of these soulful musicians. W.C. Handy, a well-schooled cornetist and bandleader, had first heard blues sung and played in the deep South in the 1890s.

In 1912 he published a musically polished and somewhat sanitized blues, the groundbreaking "Memphis Blues." Two years later, "St. Louis Blues" took the world by storm and for the next 15 years blues were one of the most important influences in pop music. In this book you'll find Handy's "Beale Street" (later called "Beale Street Blues") and "St. Louis Blues," one of the most recorded songs of all time. Other blues include Henry Busse's signature tune "Sugar Blues," and the heavily blues influenced "I Ain't Got Nobody."

In the 1880s pianists in various mid-Western cities, especially St. Louis, started playing what they called, because of the characteristic anticipated third beat of the measure, "ragged time." This was soon shortened to "ragtime" and with the publication of African-American composer Scott Joplin's "Maple Leaf Rag" in 1899, ragtime became an international craze. Even such "longhair" composers as Claude Debussy made use of ragtime figures in his "Golliwog's Cakewalk." Later composers who were influenced by ragtime were Igor Stravinsky ("L'Histoire du Soldat") and Darius Milhaud ("Le Boeuf sur le Toit"). Popular songs influenced by ragtime soon followed. There were songs about ragtime ("Alexander's Ragtime Band"), ragtime songs ("Bill Bailey, Won't You Please Come Home?") and songs that contained ragtime syncopation ("Ballin' the Jack"). Bands and orchestras of the day made instrumental arrangements of what had been strictly piano music, and after adding a touch of the blues and relaxing the strict rhythmic feel of ragtime, the Jazz Age was on its way.

The advent of jazz threw the bluestockings into a tizzy. The word itself had strong sexual connotations and it was feared that America's morals were in precipitous decline. This caused executives at Victor (now RCA) Records to spell the word "jass" on the 1917 recordings by the "Original Dixieland Jass Band." This did not prevent the ODJB from selling hundreds of thousands of records containing this new art form. They were soon followed by many other jazz artists, some great geniuses of improvisation like Louis Armstrong and Bix Beiderbecke and others who, in addition, were great jazz composers and arrangers like Duke Ellington, Jellyroll Morton and Fletcher Henderson.

This period produced many songs that have become jazz standards: "After You've Gone," "Avalon," "The Darktown Strutters' Ball," "Somebody Stole My Gal," "There'll Be Some Changes Made," that indispensable part of banjo players' repertoire, "The World is Waiting for the Sunrise" and many others which we have included.

But the main criterion we have followed in compiling this collection of songs is their relevance to modern audiences. Every song in this collection is played and sung today. The arrangements are somewhat simplified for the modern player, but never to the point of losing the original flavor of the song. And almost every one of the verses are here. In the music of that period, the verse was an intrinsic part of the song. It was used to set up the chorus, and often the song makes little sense without it.

Arranger Dan Fox has made a few changes in melodies, words, and chord progressions to reflect the way these songs are usually performed today. For example, a comparison of his arrangements of "The World is Waiting for the Sunrise" and "There'll Be Some Changes Made" with their original versions shows that Fox has changed the choruses to "long meter." That is, eighth notes in the original become quarter notes in the modern version. We've also included modern chord symbols for guitar and/or banjo players. The original editions either had no symbols at all, or printed ukulele diagrams which are of little use to the modern player.

We urge you to browse through the various indexes. If you have a favorite composer or lyric writer you'll find him or her in that index on page 10. If you can't remember the real name of a song look it up in the Index of First Lines and Key Phrases on page 13. Or maybe you'd like to have friends over for a singalong. Consult the Categorical Index on page 8 for suggestions on how to group the songs.

But even more important than all the above, is using this book as a practical way to enjoy and appreciate the music that has conquered the world, the music of America.

Categorical Index

Index of Composers and Lyricists

Goetz, E. Ray
　For Me and My Gal

Golden, John L.
　Poor Butterfly

Grey, Clifford
　If You Were the Only Girl in the
　　World

Gruber, Edmund L.
　Caisson Song

Hall, Guy
　Johnson Rag

Handy, W.C.
　Beale Street
　St. Louis Blues

Hanley, James F.
　Rose of Washington Square
　Second Hand Rose

Hawthorne, Alice (pseudonym of
　Septimus Winner)

Herbert, Victor
　Dagger Dance

Higgins, Billy
　There'll Be Some Changes Made

Hubbell, Raymond
　Poor Butterfly

Jackson, Tony
　Pretty Baby

Jacobs-Bond, Carrie
　I Love You Truly

Jolson, Al
　Avalon

Kahn, Gus
　Ain't We Got Fun

Memories
Pretty Baby

Kellette, John William
　I'm Forever Blowing Bubbles

Kenbrovin, Jaan*
　I'm Forever Blowing Bubbles

Kendis, James
　If I Had My Way

Kern, Jerome
　Look for the Silver Lining
　They Didn't Believe Me
　Till the Clouds Roll By

Klein, Lou
　If I Had My Way

Kleinkauf, Henry
　Johnson Rag

Lawlor, Charles B.
　Sidewalks of New York, The

Layton, Turner
　After You've Gone

Lehar, Franz
　Vilia

Leslie, Edgar
　For Me and My Gal

Lewis, Sam M.
　My Mammy
　Rock-A-Bye Your Baby (With a
　　Dixie Melody)

Lewis, Ted
　When My Baby Smiles at Me

Lincke, Paul
　Glow-Worm, The

*Jaan Kenbrovin was the collective pseudonym of
James Kendis, James Brockman and Nat Vincent.

Lockhart, Eugene
　World is Waiting for the Sunrise,
　　The

Macdonald, Ballard
　Beautiful Ohio
　Rose of Washington Square
　Trail of the Lonesome Pine, The

Madden, Edward
　By the Light of the Silvery Moon
　Moonlight Bay

McCarthy, Joseph
　Alice Blue Gown
　I'm Always Chasing Rainbows
　You Made Me Love You

Meyer, George W.
　For Me and My Gal

Milburn, Richard
　Listen to the Mockingbird

Miles, Capt. Alfred H.
　Anchors Aweigh

Mills, Kerry
　Meet Me in St. Louis, Louis

Mitchell, George
　Ace in the Hole

Monaco, James V. (Jimmie)
　You Made Me Love You

Munro, Bill
　When My Baby Smiles at Me

Norton, George
　My Melancholy Baby

Norworth, Jack
　Shine On Harvest Moon

Offenbach, Jacques
　Marines' Hymn, The

O'Hara, Geoffrey
  K-K-K-Katy

Olman, Abe
  Oh Johnny, Oh Johnny, Oh!

Overstreet, W. Benton
  There'll Be Some Changes Made

Paterson, A.B.
  Waltzing Matilda

Powell, Felix
  Pack Up Your Troubles in Your Old
    Kit Bag

Pryor, Arthur
  Whistler and His Dog, The

Reynolds, Herbert
  They Didn't Believe Me

Robinson, J. Russel
  Margie

Robinson, Lilla Cayley
  Glow-Worm, The

Romberg, Sigmund
  Will You Remember (Sweetheart)

Rose, Ed
  Oh Johnny, Oh Johnny, Oh!

Rose, Vincent
  Avalon
  Whispering

Ross, Adrian
  Vilia

Schonberger, John
  Whispering

Schwartz, Jean
  Rock-a-Bye Your Baby (With a
    Dixie Melody)

Scott, Clement
  Oh Promise Me

Seitz, Ernest
  World is Waiting for the Sunrise,
    The

Silvers, Louis
  April Showers

Sissle, Noble
  I'm Just Wild About Harry

Smith, Chris
  Ballin' the Jack

Smith, Harry B.
  Sheik of Araby, The

Snyder, Ted
  Sheik of Araby, The

Sterling, Andrew B.
  Meet Me in St. Louis, Louis
  When My Baby Smiles at Me

Taylor, Tell
  Down by the Old Mill Stream

Tierney, Harry
  Alice Blue Gown

Van Alstyne, Egbert
  Memories
  Pretty Baby

Von Tilzer, Harry
  I Want a Girl (Just Like the Girl
    That Married Dear Old Dad)
  When My Baby Smiles at Me

Warfield, Charles
  I Ain't Got Nobody

Weatherly, Fred E.
  Roses of Picardy

Wenrich, Percy
  Moonlight Bay

Wheeler, Francis
  Sheik of Araby, The

Whiting, Richard A.
  Ain't We Got Fun
  Japanese Sandman, The
  Till We Meet Again

Whitson, Beth Slater
  Let Me Call You Sweetheart

Williams, Clarence
  Sugar Blues

Williams, Spencer
  Tishomingo Blues

Winner, Septimus
  Listen to the Mockingbird

Wodehouse, P.D.
  Till the Clouds Roll By

Wood, Haydn
  Roses of Picardy

Wood, Leo
  Somebody Stole My Gal

Young, David
  I Ain't Got Nobody

Young, Joe
  My Mammy
  Rock-a-Bye Your Baby (With a
    Dixie Melody)

Young, Rida Johnson
  Will You Remember (Sweetheart)

Zimmerman, Charles A.
  Anchors Aweigh

Index of First Lines and Key Phrases

The first lines of every verse and chorus are listed. In addition, we have included certain key phrases by which a song may be recognized. The name of the song appears in parentheses after each.

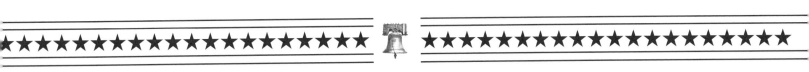

For Me & My Gal
and other Singalong Songs

April Showers
By the Light of the Silvery Moon
Down By the Old Mill Stream
For Me and My Gal
Moonlight Bay
My Melancholy Baby
Rock-a-Bye Your Baby (With a Dixie Melody)
Swanee
The Trail of the Lonesome Pine
You Made Me Love You (I Didn't Want to Do It)

For Me and My Gal

Words by
EDGAR LESLIE and RAY GOETZ
Music by
GEORGE W. MEYER

Copyright © 1997 by Carl Fischer, Inc.

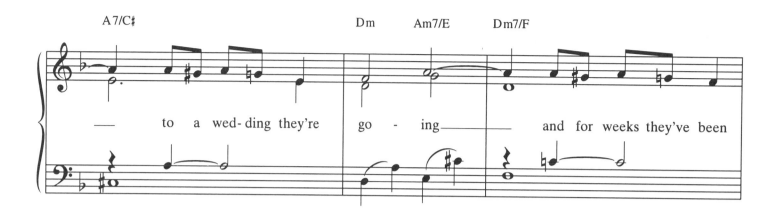

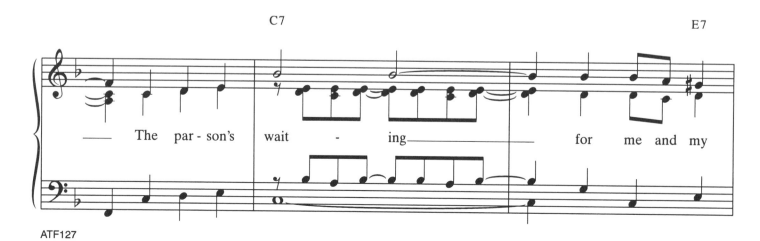

ATF127

April Showers

Words by
B. G. DeSYLVA
Music by
LOUIS SILVERS

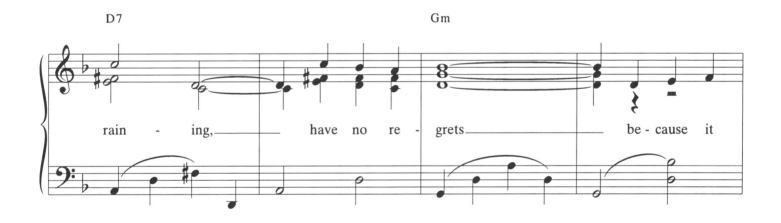

Down by the Old Mill Stream

Words and Music by
TELL TAYLOR

Slow waltz

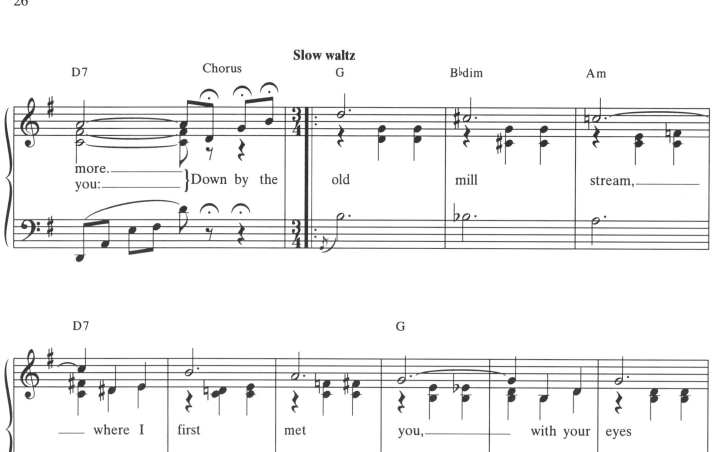

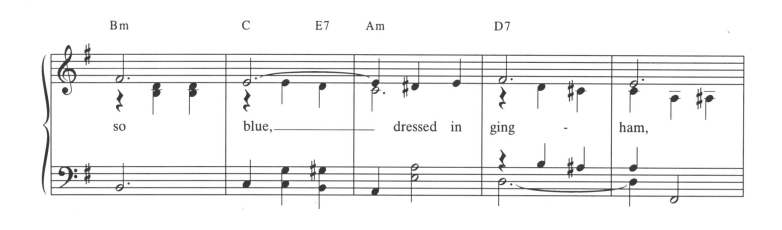

loved me true. You were six-

teen, my vil-lage queen,

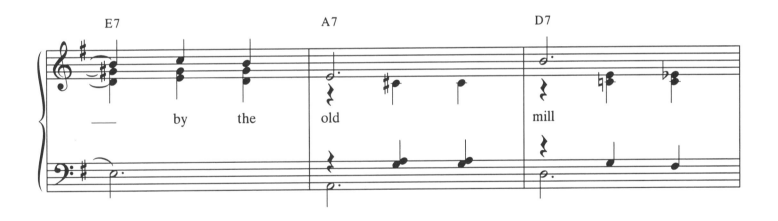

by the old mill

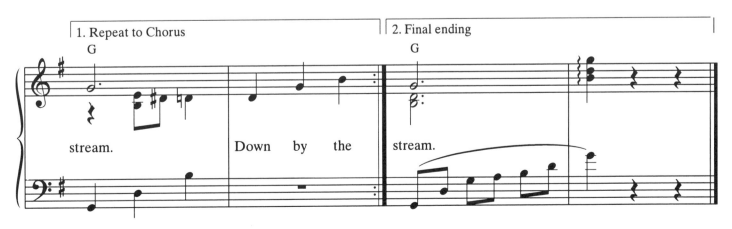

1. Repeat to Chorus

stream. Down by the

2. Final ending

stream.

ATF127

By the Light of the Silvery Moon

Words by
ED MADDEN
Music by
GUS EDWARDS

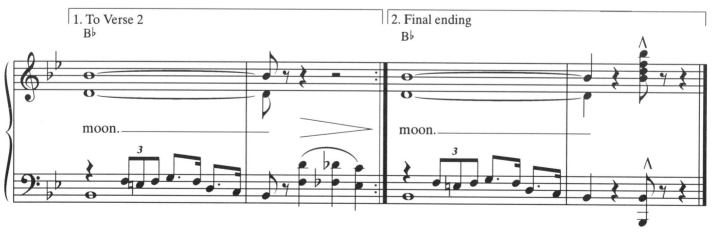

Moonlight Bay

Words by
ED MADDEN
Music by
PERCY WENRICH

Moderate soft-shoe tempo

Voic - es
Can - dle

hum, croon - ing o - ver Moon - light Bay._____
lights gleam - ing on the si - lent shore._____

Ban - jos strum, tun - ing while the moon - beams
Lone - ly nights, dream - ing till we meet once

play._____ All a - lone,_____ un - known_____ they find me;
more._____ Far a - part,_____ her heart_____ is yearn - ing,

Copyright © 1997 by Carl Fischer, Inc.

Mem - o - ries ___ like these ___ re - mind me of the girl ___ I left ___
with a sigh ___ for my ___ re - turn - ing with the light ___ of love ___

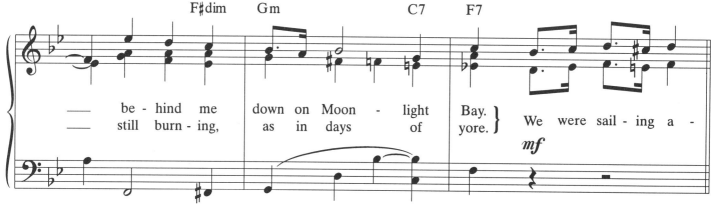

___ be - hind me down on Moon - light Bay.
___ still burn - ing, as in days of yore. } We were sail - ing a -

Chorus:

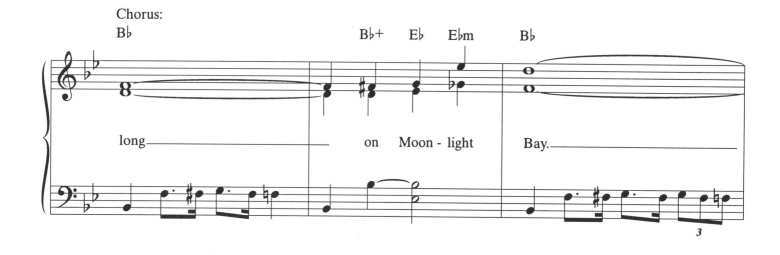

long ___ on Moon - light Bay. ___

___ We could hear the voic - es ring - ing, ___ they seemed to

Melancholy
(later known as "My Melancholy Baby")

Words by
GEORGE A. NORTON

Music by
ERNIE BURNETT

Copyright © 1997 by Carl Fischer, Inc.

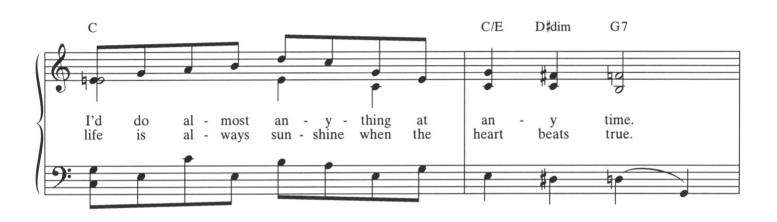

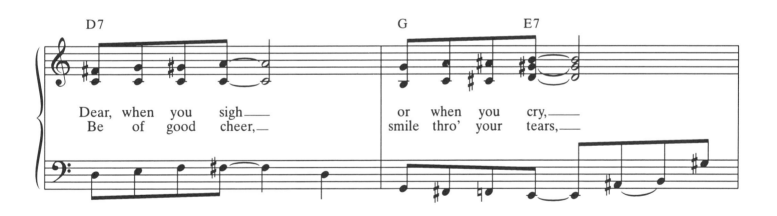

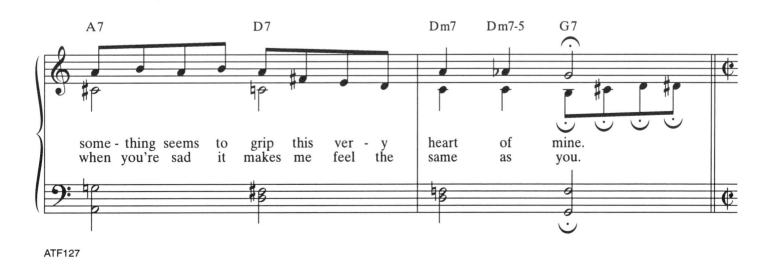

ATF127

Smoothly, in two

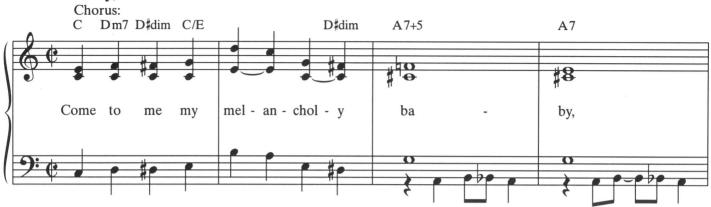

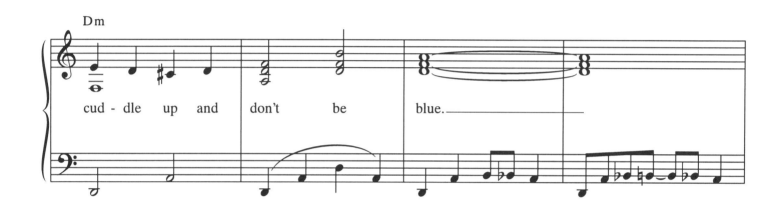

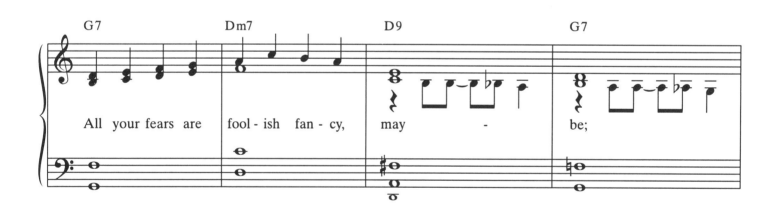

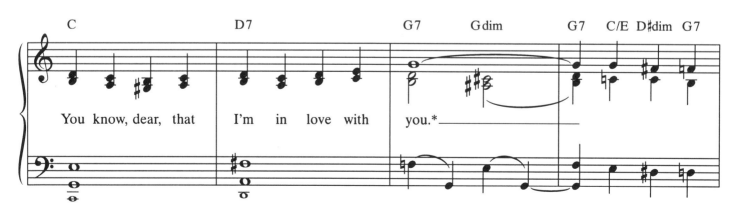

*Original words were "You know, dear, that I am strong for you."

Rock-a-Bye Your Baby with a Dixie Melody

Words by
SAM LEWIS and JOE YOUNG
Music by
JEAN SCHWARTZ

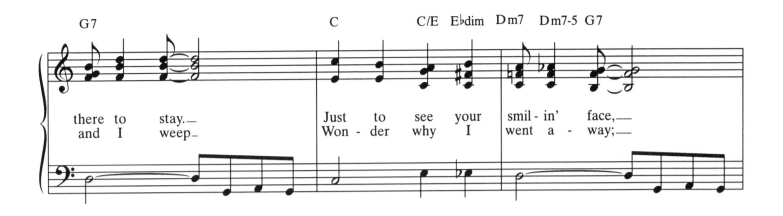

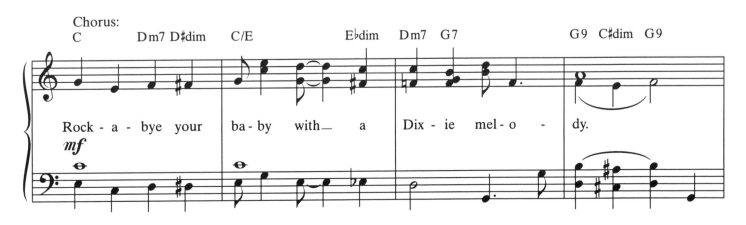

Swanee

Words by
IRVING CAESAR
Music by
GEORGE GERSHWIN

You Made Me Love You

Words by
JOE McCARTHY
Music by
JIMMIE MONACO

Copyright © 1997 by Carl Fischer, Inc.

47

ATF127

The Trail of the Lonesome Pine

Words by
BALLARD MACDONALD
Music by
HARRY CARROLL

Moderately

Verse:

On a moun - tain in Vir - gin - i - a
I can hear the tink - ling wa - ter - fall,

stands a lone - some pine.
far a - mong the hills.

Just be - low
Blue - birds sing

is the cab - in home of a lit - tle girl of mine. Her
each so mer - ri - ly to his mate in rap - ture trills. They

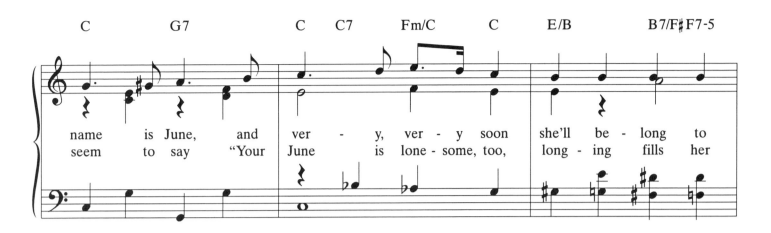

name   is June,   and   ver - y, ver - y soon   she'll be - long   to
seem   to say   "Your   June   is lone - some, too,   long - ing fills her

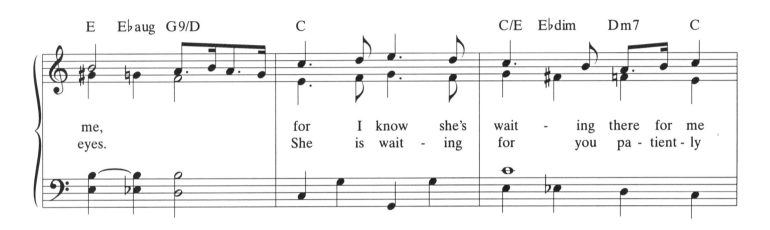

me,   for   I know she's   wait - ing there for me
eyes.   She   is wait - ing   for   you pa - tient - ly

Chorus:

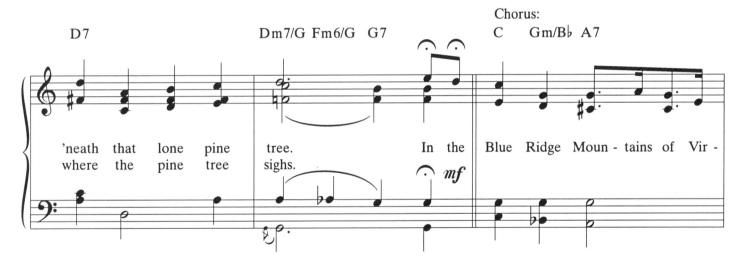

'neath that lone pine   tree.   In the   Blue Ridge Moun - tains of Vir -
where the pine tree   sighs.

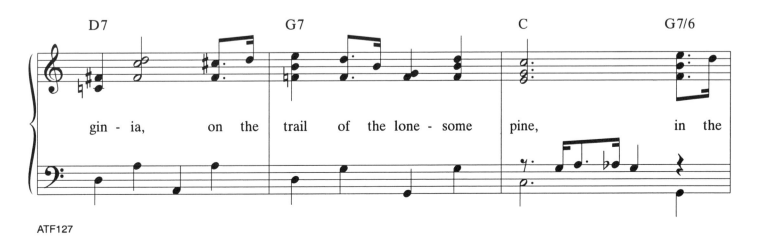

gin - ia,   on the   trail of the lone - some   pine,   in the

Broadway Shows, Operettas & The Vaudeville Stage

Alice Blue Gown (from "Irene")
Give My Regards to Broadway (from "Little Johnny Jones")
I'm Just Wild About Harry (from "Shuffle Along")
Look for the Silver Lining (from "Sally")
Oh Promise Me (from "Robin Hood")
Poor Butterfly (from "The Big Show")
Pretty Baby (from "The Passing Show of 1916")
Rose of Washington Square
Second Hand Rose
Shine On, Harvest Moon (from "The Follies of 1908")
They Didn't Believe Me (from "The Girl from Utah")
Till the Clouds Roll By (from "Oh Boy!")
The Yankee Doodle Boy (from "Little Johnny Jones")
Villa (from the operetta "The Merry Widow")
Will You Remember (Sweetheart) (from "Maytime")
You're a Grand Old Flag (from "George Washington, Jr.")

Alice Blue Gown

Words by
JOSEPH McCARTHY
Music by
HARRY TIERNEY

Give My Regards to Broadway

By
GEORGE M. COHAN

Bright march tempo

I'm Just Wild About Harry

Words and Music by
NOBLE SISSLE and
EUBIE BLAKE

*lamps = eyes

Oh Promise Me

Words by
CLEMENT SCOTT
Music by
REGINALD DeKOVEN

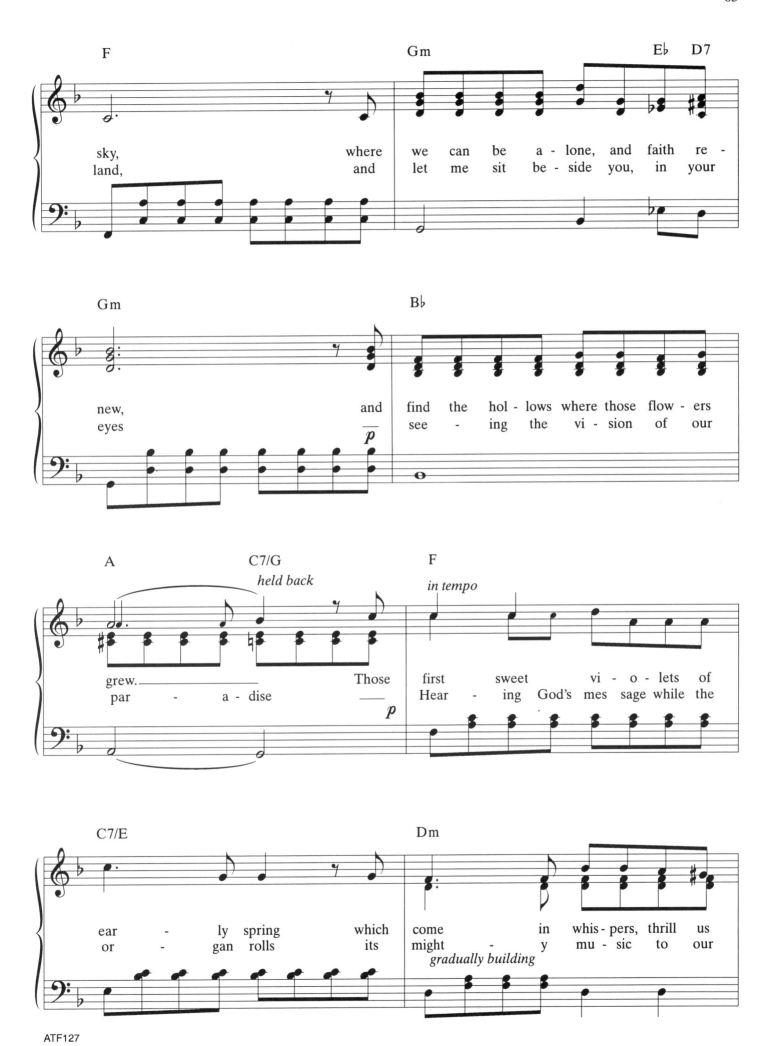

64

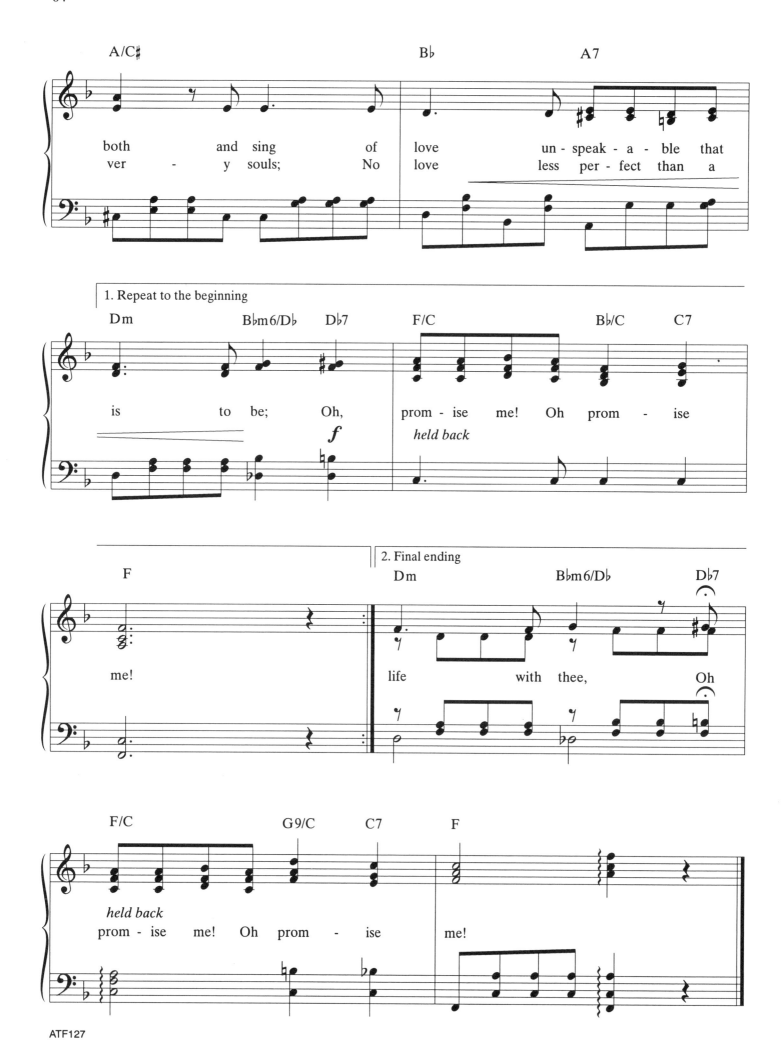

ATF127

Look for the Silver Lining

Words by
BUDDY DeSYLVA
Music by
JEROME KERN

Freely

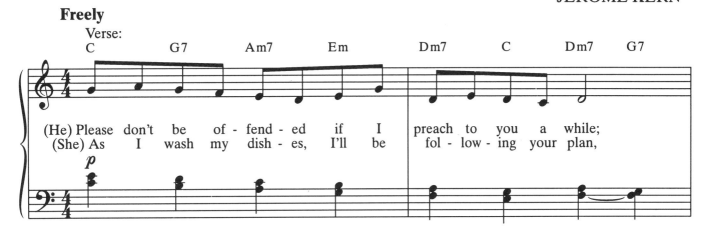

(He) Please don't be of-fend-ed if I preach to you a while;
(She) As I wash my dish-es, I'll be fol-low-ing your plan,

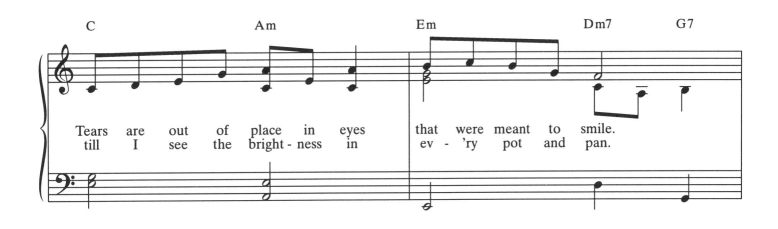

Tears are out of place in eyes that were meant to smile.
till I see of the bright-ness in ev-'ry pot and pan.

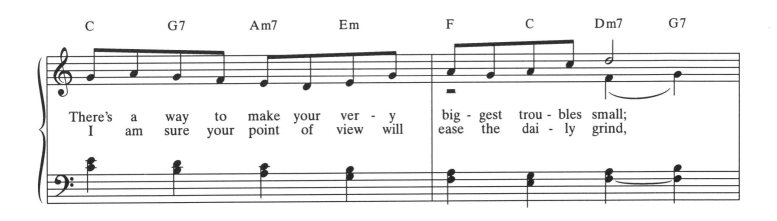

There's a way to make your ver-y big-gest trou-bles small;
I am sure your point of view will ease the dai-ly grind,

Poor Butterfly

Words by
JOHN L. GOLDEN
Music by
RAYMOND HUBBELL

Copyright © 1997 by Carl Fischer, Inc.

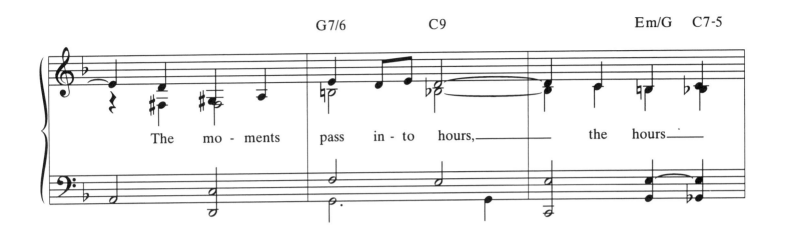

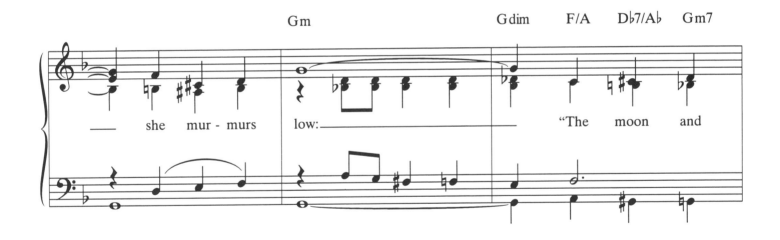

Pretty Baby

Words by
GUS KAHN
Music by
TONY JACKSON and
EGBERT VAN ALSTYNE

Rose of Washington Square

Words by
BALLARD MacDONALD
Music by
JAMES F. HANLEY

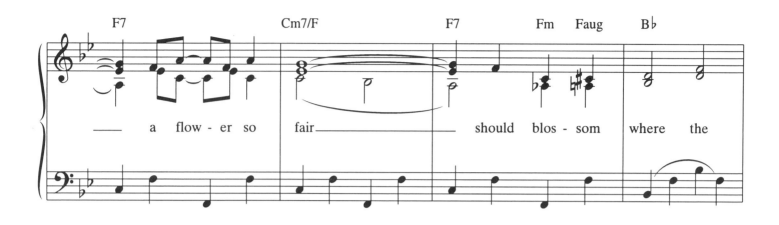

a flow-er so fair_____ should blos-som where the

sun shines. Rose,_____ for na-ture did not mean_____

_____ that you should blush un-seen,_____ but be the queen of

some fair gar-den. Rose,_____ I'll nev-er de-part,_____

Second Hand Rose

Words by
GRANT CLARKE
Music by
JAMES F. HANLEY

ATF127

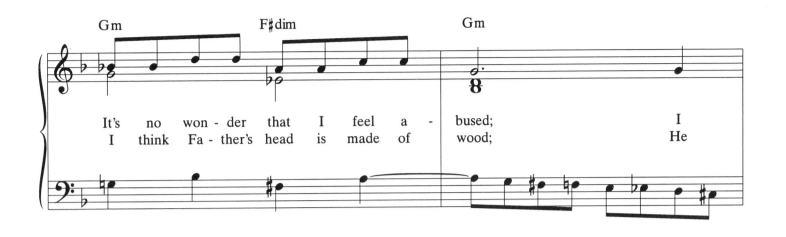

Gm   F#dim   Gm

It's no won-der that I feel a-bused;   I
I think Fa-ther's head is made of wood;   He

Dm7   G9   Bb/C   C7

nev-er have a thing that ain't been used.____ I'm wear-ing
brings home lots of things that ain't no good.____ I'm wear-ing

mf

Moderately, in 2
Chorus:

F   G7

Sec-ond hand hats,____   sec-ond hand clothes;____
sec-ond hand shoes,____   sec-ond hand hose;____

C7

____   That's why they call____   me____
____   All the girls hand____   me their

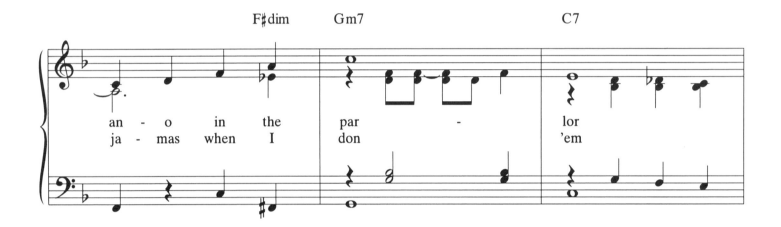

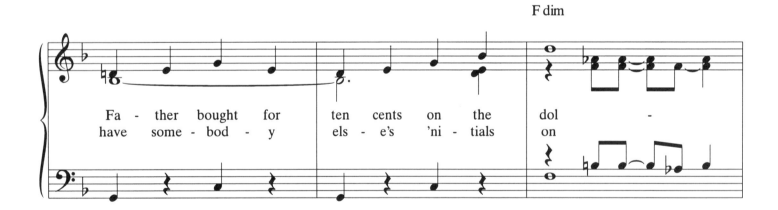

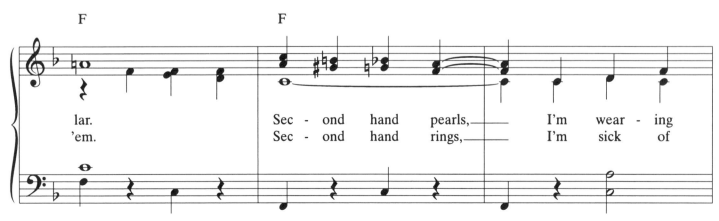

Guide to 1920's expressions: Second Avenue = District in New York City that became the home
for many Jewish immigrants. In the 20's it was the heart of the Yiddish theater; Kicks the whole
day long = complains incessantly; beaux (pronounced "boze") = boy friends; got my goat = annoyed me.

Shine On, Harvest Moon

Words by
JACK NORWORTH
Music by
NORA BAYES-NORWORTH

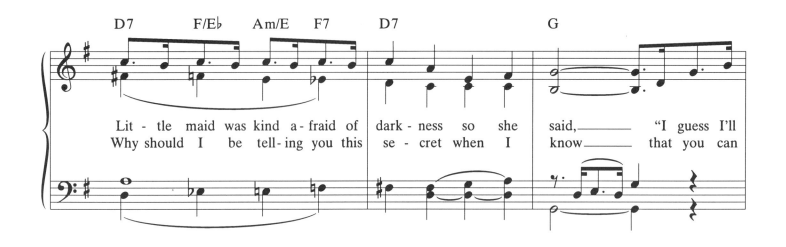

Lit - tle maid was kind a - fraid of darkness so she said,____ "I guess I'll
Why should I be tell-ing you this se - cret when I know____ that you can

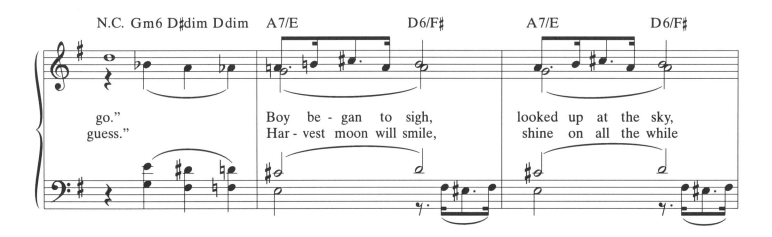

go." Boy be - gan to sigh, looked up at the sky,
guess." Har - vest moon will smile, shine on all the while

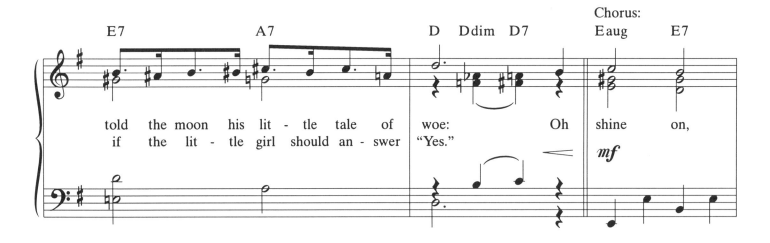

told the moon his lit - tle tale of woe: Oh shine on,
if the lit - tle girl should an - swer "Yes."

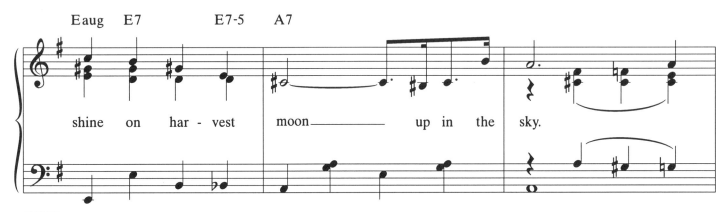

shine on har - vest moon____ up in the sky.

They Didn't Believe Me

Words by
HERBERT REYNOLDS
Music by
JEROME KERN

Moderately

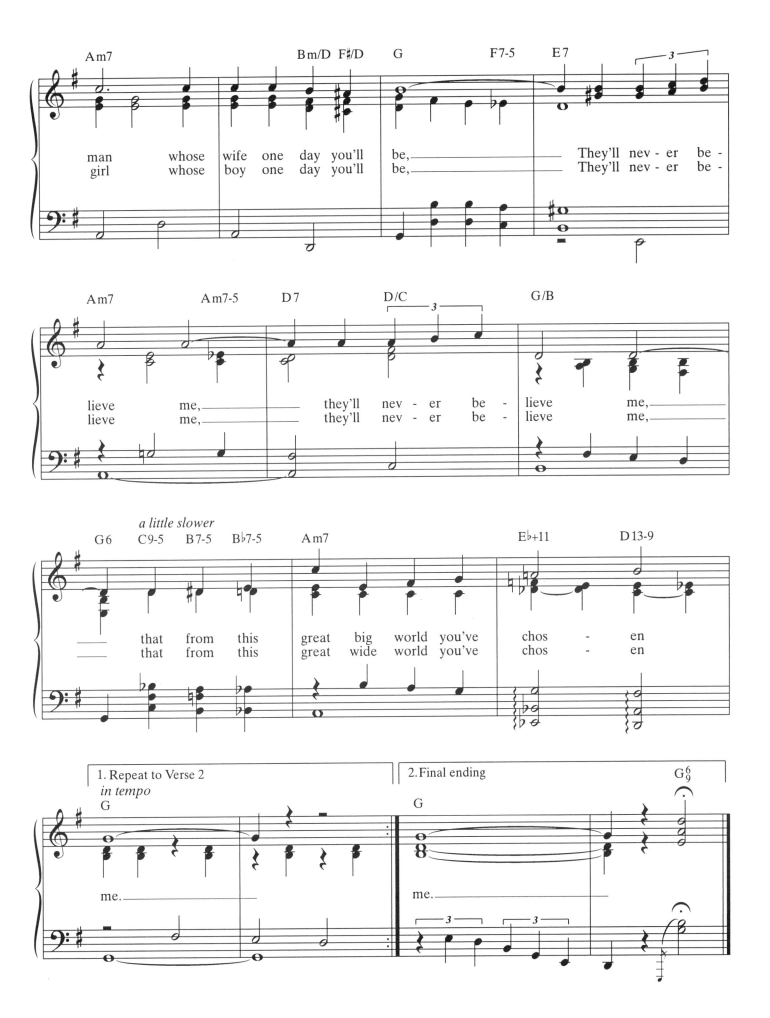

Till the Clouds Roll By

Words by
P.G. WODEHOUSE and GUY BOLTON
Music by
JEROME KERN

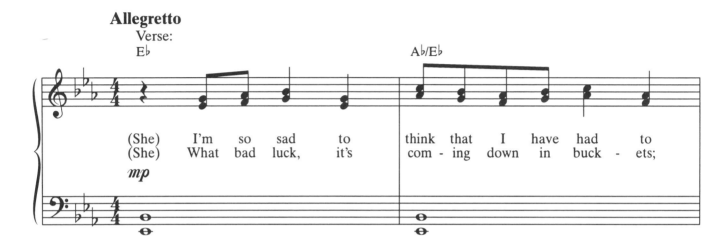

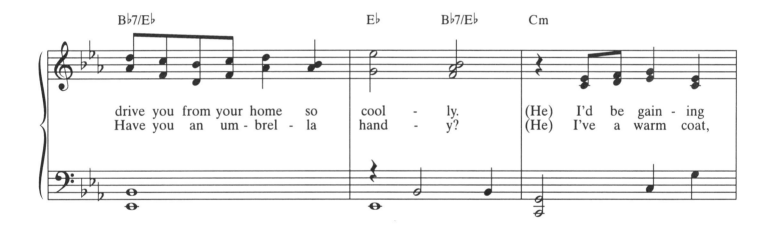

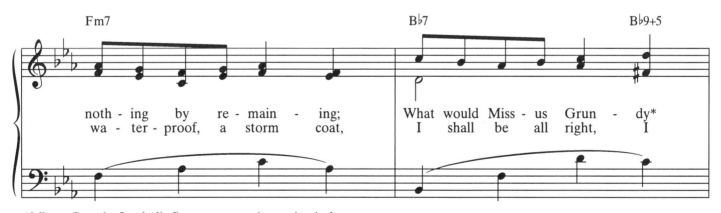

*Missus Grundy: Symbolic figure representing puritanical mores.

say?
know.
Her con - ven - tions,
La - ter on, too,
kind - ly re - col - lect them!
I will ward the grippe off

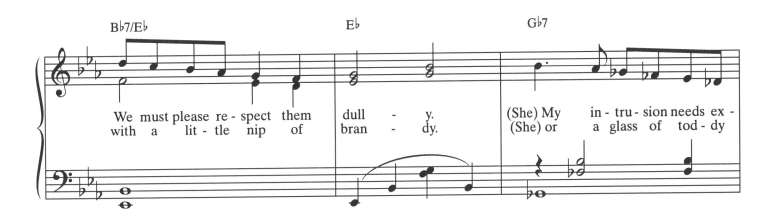

We must please re - spect them
with a lit - tle nip of
dull - y.
bran - dy.
(She) My
(She) or
in - tru - sion needs ex -
a glass of tod - dy

plain - ing:
drain - ing,
I felt my cour - age
you'd find that more sus -
wan - ing.
tain - ing.

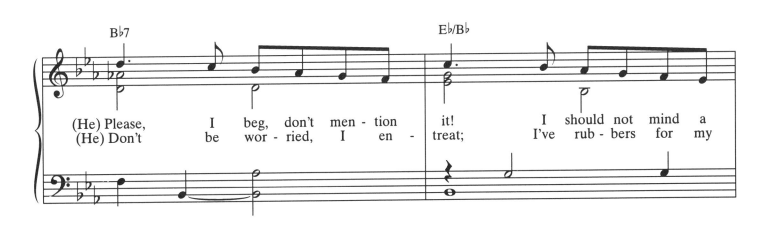

(He) Please,
(He) Don't
I beg, don't men - tion
be wor - ried, I en - treat;
it!
I should not mind a
I've rub - bers for my

Vilia

Words by
ADRIAN ROSS
Music by
FRANZ LEHAR

Copyright © 1997 by Carl Fischer, Inc.

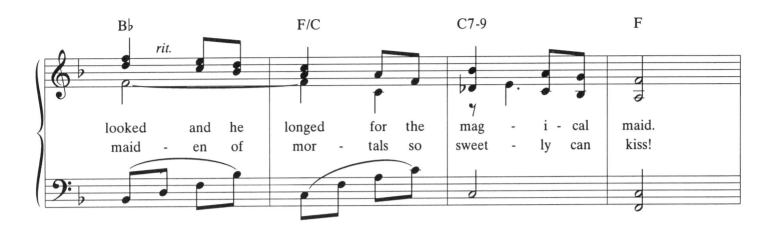

looked   and he   longed   for the   mag   -   i - cal   maid.
maid - en of   mor - tals so   sweet - ly can   kiss!

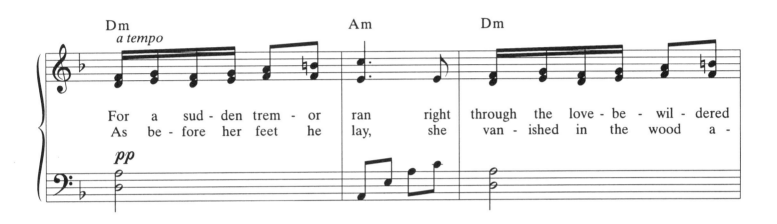

For a sud - den trem - or   ran   right   through the love - be - wil - dered
As be - fore her feet he   lay,   she   van - ished in the wood a -

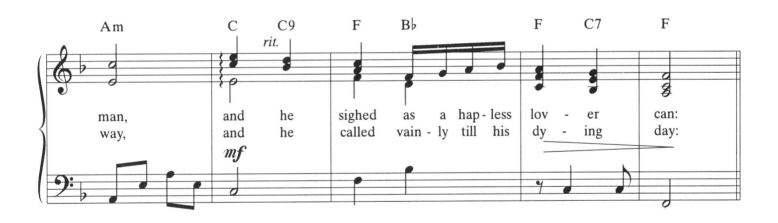

man,   and he   sighed as a hap - less   lov - er   can:
way,   and he   called vain - ly till his   dy - ing   day:

Chorus:

"Vil - ia, O   Vil - ia, the   witch of the   wood,   would I not

Will You Remember
(Sweetheart)

Words by
RIDA JOHNSON YOUNG
Music by
SIGMUND ROMBERG

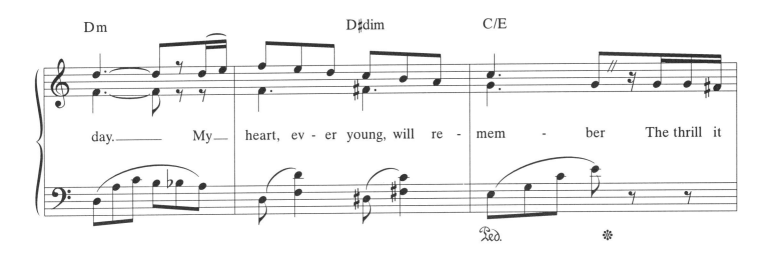

day._____ My__ heart, ev - er young, will re - mem - ber The thrill it

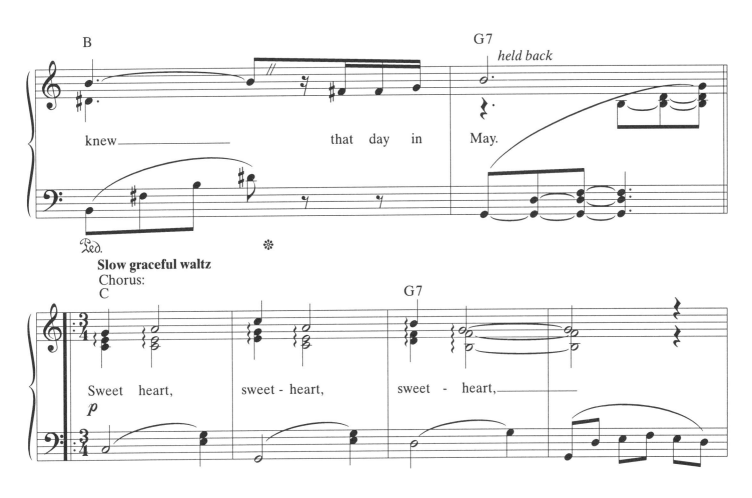

knew_____ that day in May.

Slow graceful waltz
Chorus:

Sweet heart, sweet - heart, sweet - heart,_____

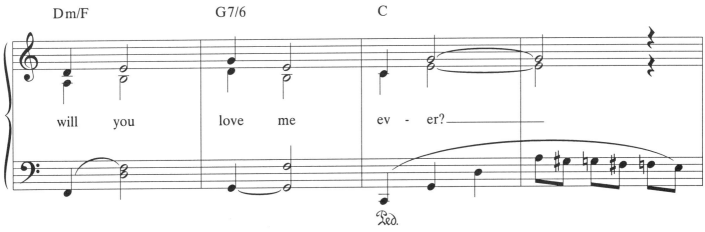

will you love me ev - er?_____

The Yankee Doodle Boy
(I'm a Yankee Doodle Dandy)

Words and Music by
GEORGE M. COHAN

Moderately march tempo

I'm the kid that's all the can-dy,
I'm a Yan-kee doo-dle dan-dy,
Fa-ther's name was Hez-i-ki-ah,
Moth-er's name was Ann Ma-ri-a,

I'm glad I am
Yanks through and through

(So's Un-cle Sam).
(Red, white, and blue!)

I'm a real live Yan-kee Doo-dle, made my name and fame and boo-dle*,
Fa-ther was so Yan-kee-heart-ed, when the Span-ish war was start-ed,

*boodle = a pile of money

ATF127

born on the Fourth of Ju - ly.___ I've
got a Yan - kee doo - dle sweet - heart,
she's my Yan - kee doo - dle joy.___ Yan - kee Doo - dle
came to Lon - don just to ride the po - nies; I am the Yan - kee Doo - dle

1. Repeat to Verse 2

2. Final ending

Boy.

Boy.

You're a Grand Old Flag

Words and Music by
GEORGE M. COHAN

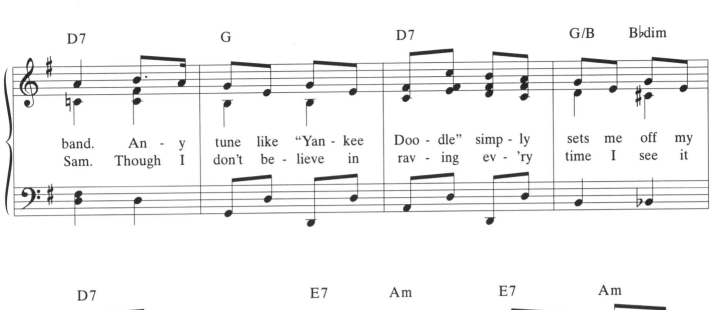

band. An - y tune like "Yan - kee Doo - dle" simp - ly sets me off my
Sam. Though I don't be - lieve in rav - ing ev - 'ry time I see it

noo - dle; It's that pa - tri - ot - ic some - thing that no
wav - ing, there's a chill runs up my back that makes me

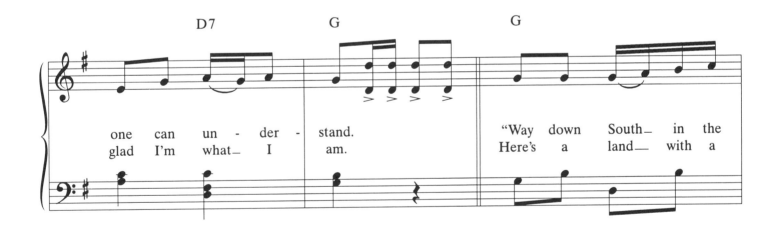

one can un - der - stand. "Way down South__ in the
glad I'm what__ I am. Here's a land__ with a

land of cot - ton," mel - o - dy un - tir - ing;__
mil - lion sol - diers; That's__ if we should need 'em,__

ATF127

*G.A.R. = Grand Army of the Republic; an association of Union Veterans of the Civil War,

Waltzes and Tearjerkers

All By Myself
Beautiful Ohio
I Love You Truly
If I Had My Way
If You Were the Only Girl in the World
I'm Always Chasing Rainbows
I'm Forever Blowing Bubbles
Let Me Call You Sweetheart
Let the Rest of the World Go By
Memories
My Gal Sal
My Mammy
Roses of Picardy
Till We Meet Again
When My Baby Smiles At Me

Beautiful Ohio

Words by
BALLARD Mac DONALD
Music by
MARY EARL

All By Myself

Words and Music By
IRVING BERLIN

Moderately, and somewhat freely

I Love You Truly

Words and Music by
CARRIE JACOBS-BOND

Copyright © 1997 by Carl Fischer, Inc.

If You Were the Only Girl in the World

Words by
CLIFFORD GREY
Music by
NAT D. AYER

124

ATF127

I'm Always Chasing Rainbows

Words by
JOSEPH McCARTHY
Music by
HARRY CARROLL

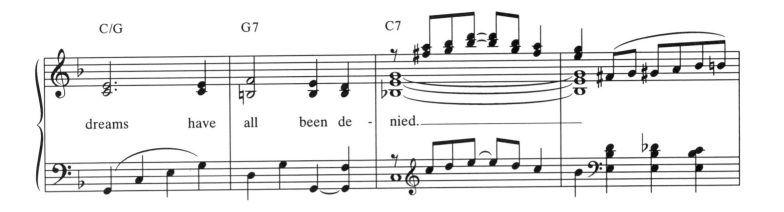

dreams have all been de - nied._____

Why have I al - ways been a fail - ure? What can the rea - son

be? I won - der if the world's to blame? I

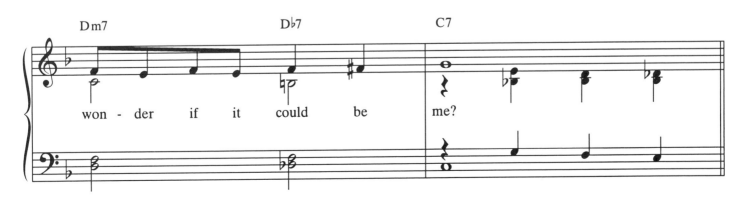

won - der if it could be me?

ATF127

If I Had My Way

Words by
LOU KLEIN
Music by
JAMES KENDIS

Copyright © 1997 by Carl Fischer, Inc.

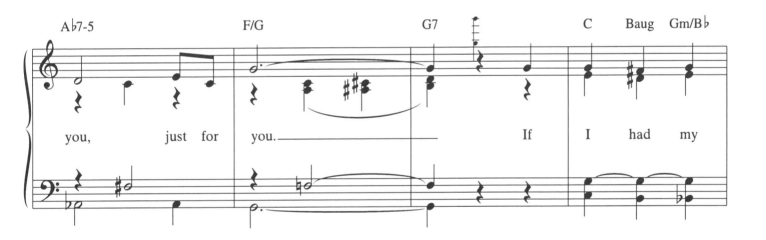

bring ev - 'ry day.____ You would reign all a - lone like a

1. Repeat to verse 2 (D.C.)

queen on a throne, if I had my

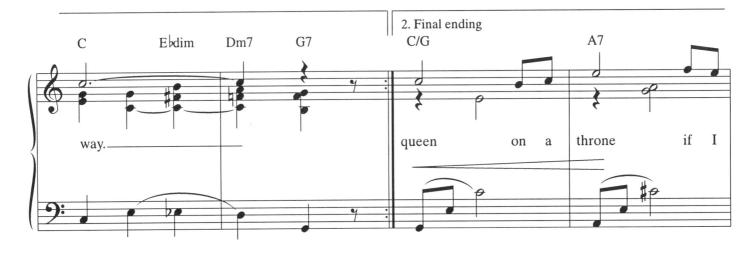

2. Final ending

way.____ queen on a throne if I

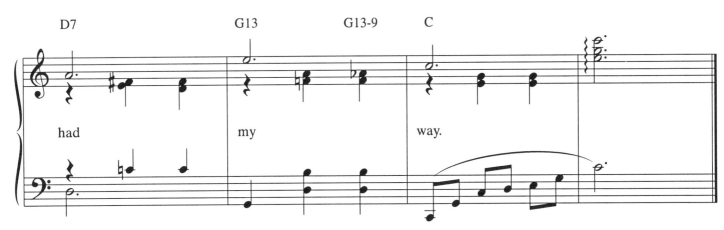

had my way.

I'm Forever Blowing Bubbles

By
JAAN KENBROVIN and
JOHN W. KELLETTE

Copyright © 1997 by Carl Fischer, Inc.

Let the Rest of the World Go By

Words by
J. KEIRN BRENNAN
Music by
ERNEST R. BALL

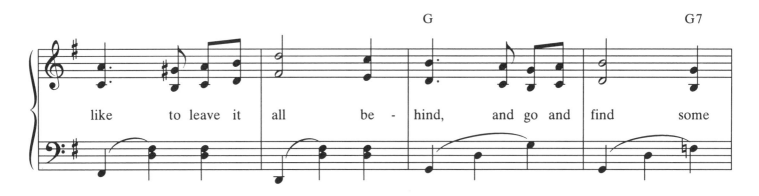

Let Me Call You Sweetheart

Words by
BETH SLATER WHITSON
Music by
LEO FRIEDMAN

My Mammy

Words by
SAM LEWIS and JOE YOUNG
Music by
WALTER DONALDSON

Memories

Words by
GUS KAHN
Music by
EGBERT VAN ALSTYNE

Copyright © 1997 by Carl Fischer, Inc.

My Gal Sal
(They Called Her Frivolous Sal)

Words and Music by
PAUL DRESSER

Freely, in four

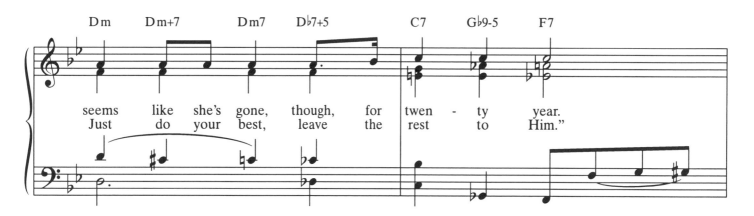

Copyright © 1997 by Carl Fischer, Inc.

Oh, how I miss her, my old pal.
Gent-ly I pressed her to my breast;
Oh, how I'd kiss her,
Soon she would take her

my gal Sal.
last long rest.
Face, not so hand-some, but
She looked at me and _
eyes, don't you know,
mur-mured, "Pal."
that
And

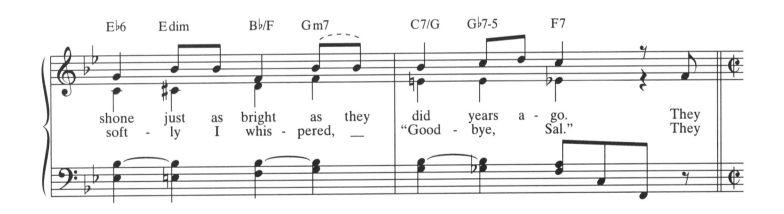

shone just as bright as they
soft-ly I whis-pered, _
did years a-go.
"Good-bye, Sal."
They
They

Moderately, in two

Chorus:

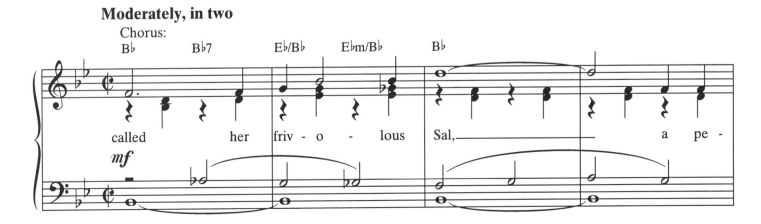

called her friv-o-lous Sal, a pe-

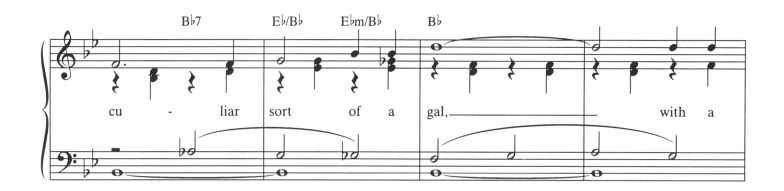

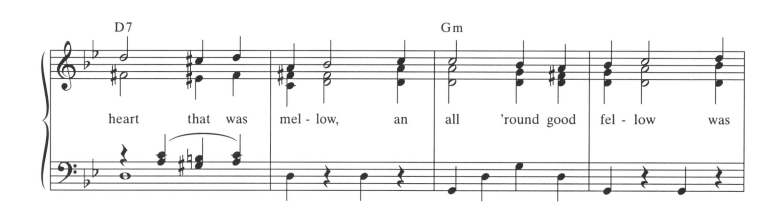

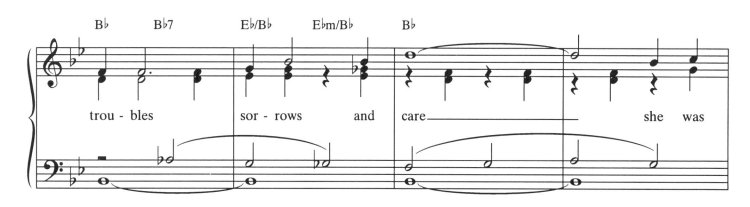

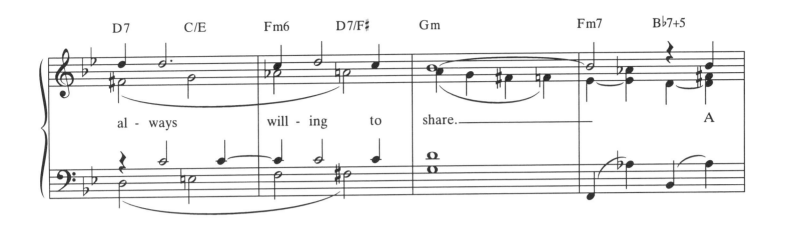

al - ways   will - ing to   share._____   A

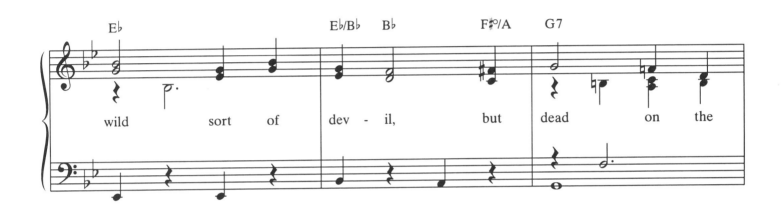

wild   sort of   dev - il,   but   dead   on the

lev - el   was   my   gal

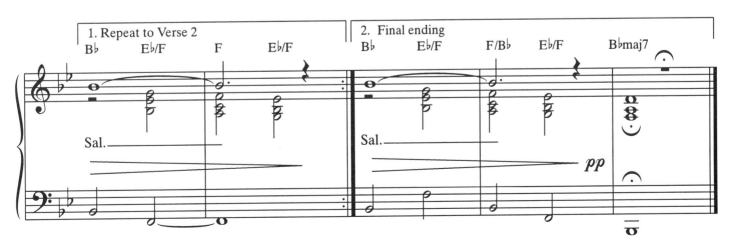

1. Repeat to Verse 2

2. Final ending

Sal._____

Sal._____

pp

ATF127

Roses of Picardy

Words by
FRED E. WEATHERLY
Music by
HAYDN WOOD

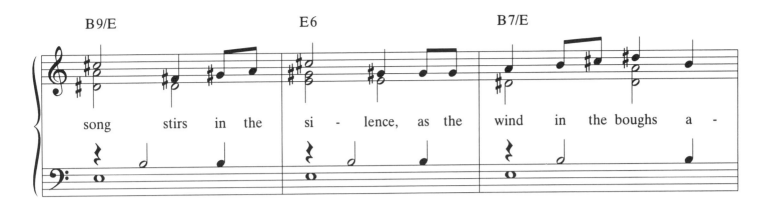

song stirs in the si - lence, as the wind in the boughs a -

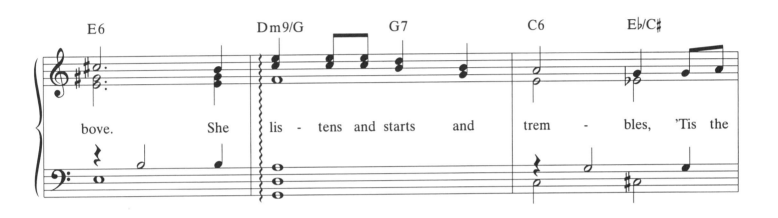

bove. She lis - tens and starts and trem - bles, 'Tis the

Smoothly in 2
Chorus:

first lit - tle song of love: "Ros - es are

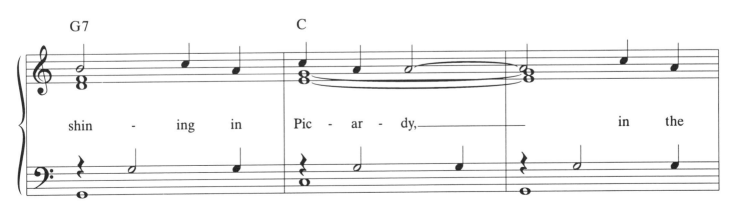

shin - ing in Pic - ar - dy,_____ in the

ATF127

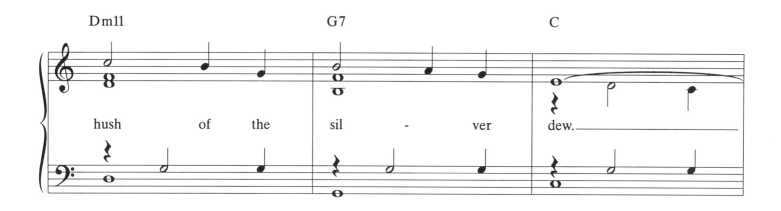

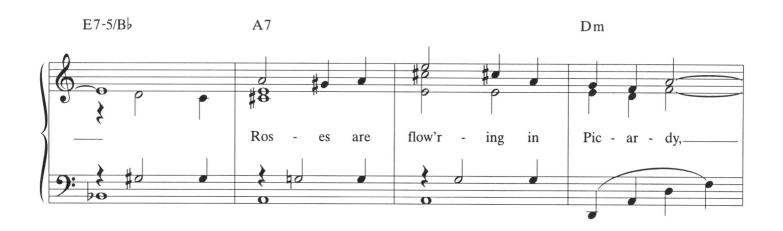

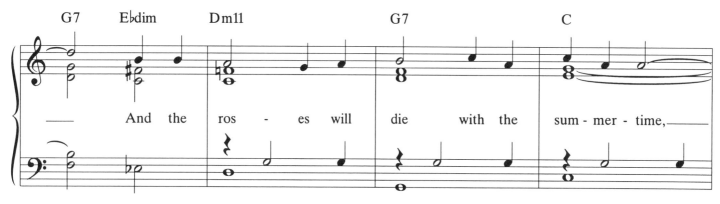

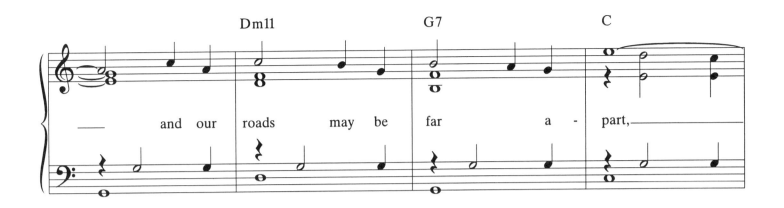

and our roads may be far a - part,

But there's one rose that dies not in Pic - ar - dy,

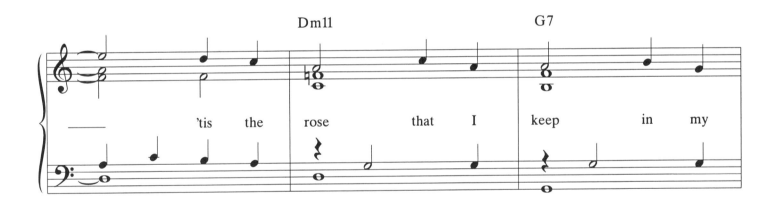

'tis the rose that I keep in my

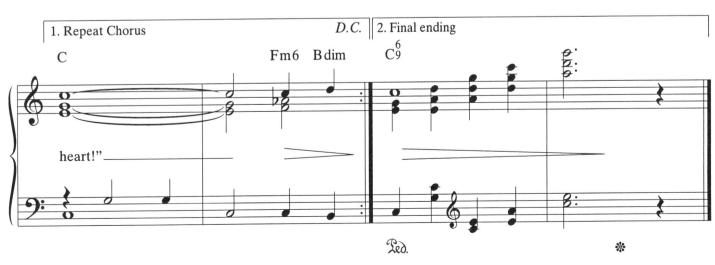

heart!"

ATF127

Till We Meet Again

Words by
RAYMOND B. EGAN
Music by
RICHARD A. WHITING

*land of the lily = France

Copyright © 1997 by Carl Fischer, Inc.

When My Baby Smiles at Me

By
HARRY VON TILZER,
ANDREW B. STERLING,
BILL MUNRO and TED LEWIS

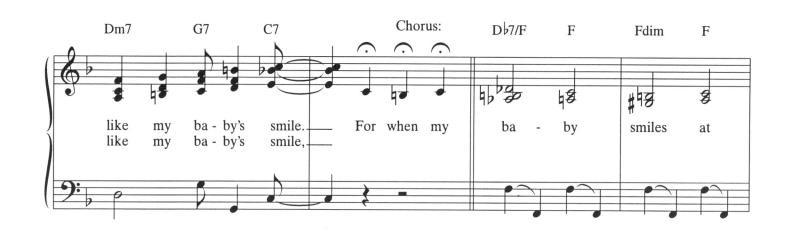

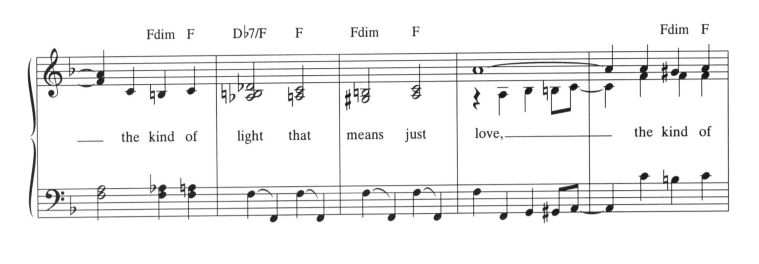

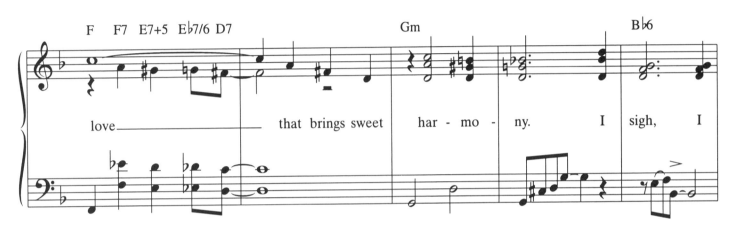

ATF127

Hot Jazz Standards & Blues

After You've Gone

Words by
HENRY CREAMER
Music by
TURNER LAYTON

Alexander's Ragtime Band

Words and Music by
IRVING BERLIN

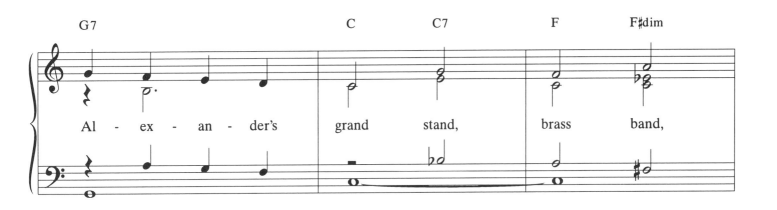

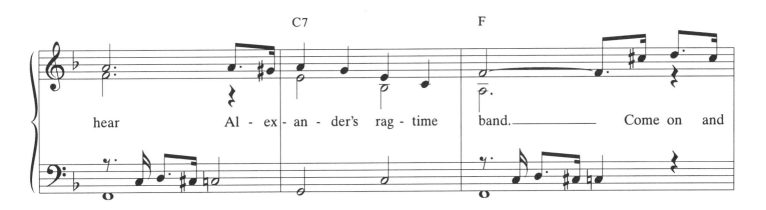

hand＿＿ up to the man＿＿ up to the man who's the lead-er of the

band.＿＿＿＿＿ And if you care to hear the Swa-nee Riv-er

played in rag-time,＿ come on and hear,＿＿ come on and

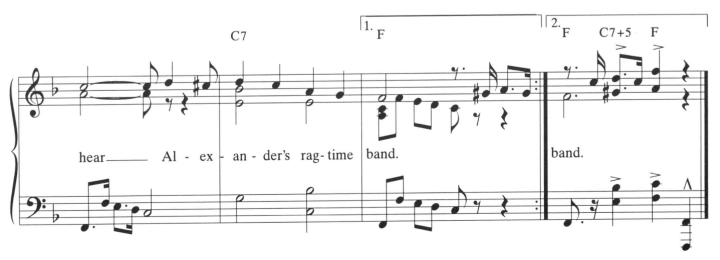

hear＿＿ Al-ex-an-der's rag-time band. band.

Ballin' the Jack

Words by
JIM BURRIS
Music by
CHRIS SMITH

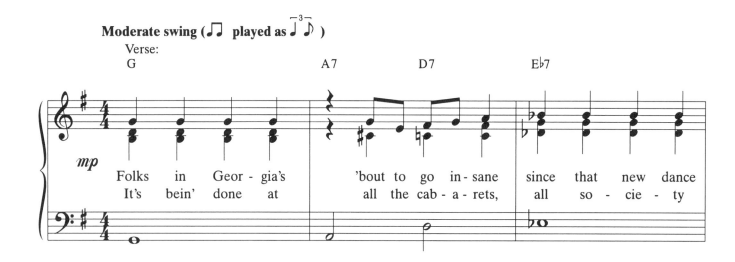

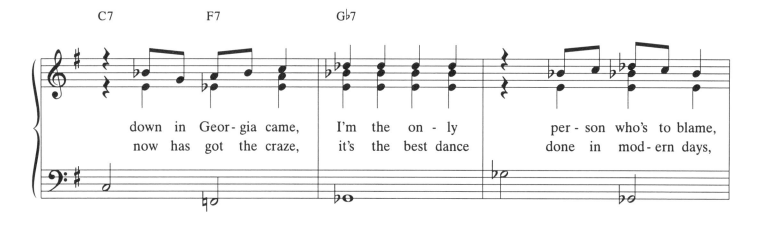

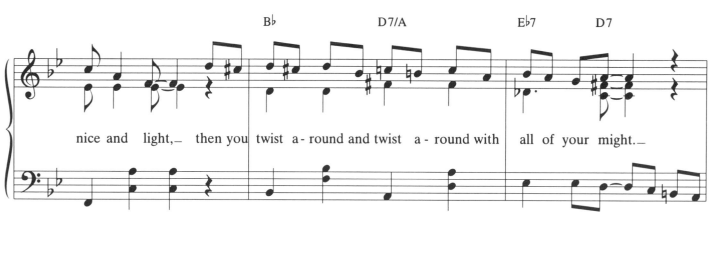

nice and light,— then you twist a-round and twist a-round with all of your might.—

Stretch your lov-in' arms straight out in space,— then you do the Ea-gle Rock with sty-

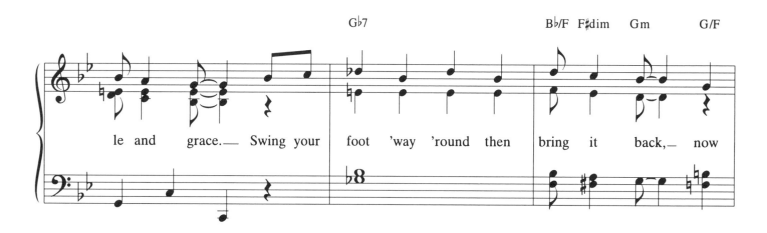

le and grace.— Swing your foot 'way 'round then bring it back,— now

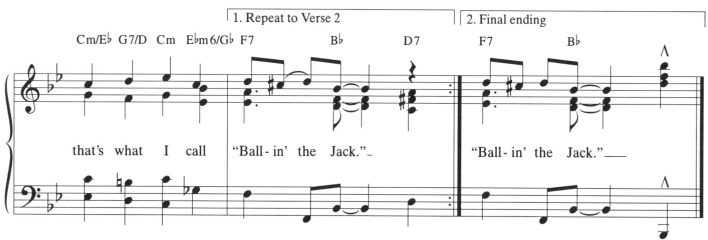

that's what I call "Ball-in' the Jack."— "Ball-in' the Jack."——

Avalon

Words by
AL JOLSON and B. G. DeSYLVA
Music by
VINCENT ROSE

Copyright © 1997 by Carl Fischer, Inc.

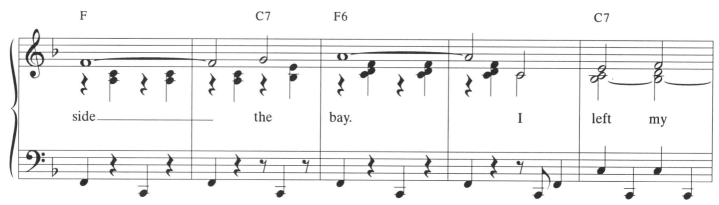

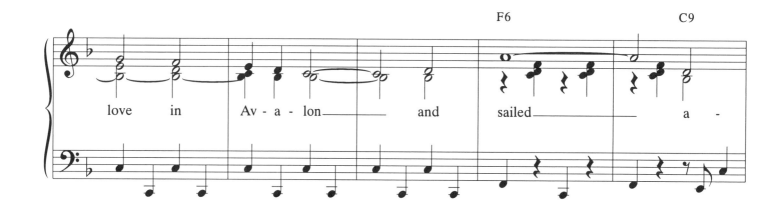

Beale Street

Words and Music by
W.C. HANDY

Copyright © 1997 by Carl Fischer, Inc.

2nd strain

G   C   G   D7   E dim

Beale Street could talk,— if Beale Street could talk,— mar - ried men would have to take their

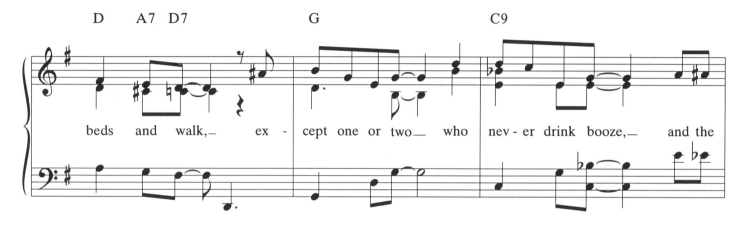

D   A7   D7   G   C9

beds and walk,— ex - cept one or two— who nev - er drink booze,— and the

G

blind man on the cor - ner who— sings the Beale Street Blues. I'd rath - er

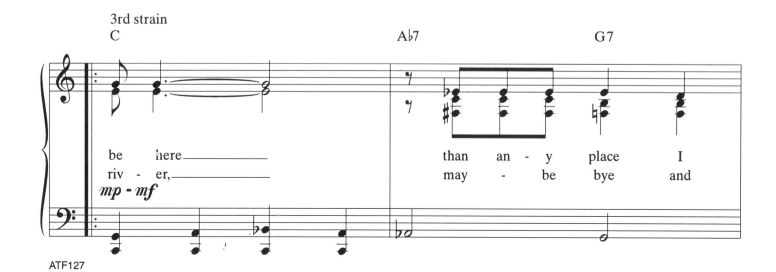

3rd strain

C   A♭7   G7

be here_____ than an - y place I
riv - er,_____ may - be bye and

mp - mf

Dardanella

By
FRED FISHER,
FELIX BERNARD and
JOHNNY S. BLACK

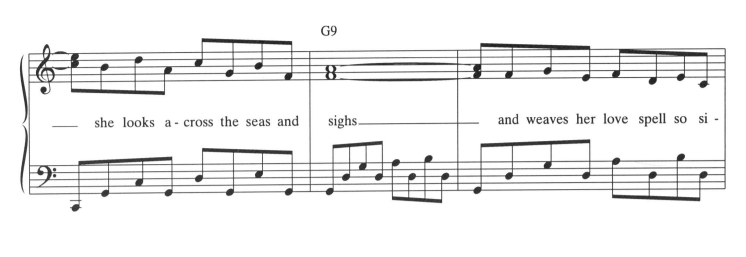

she looks a-cross the seas and sighs_____ and weaves her love spell so si-

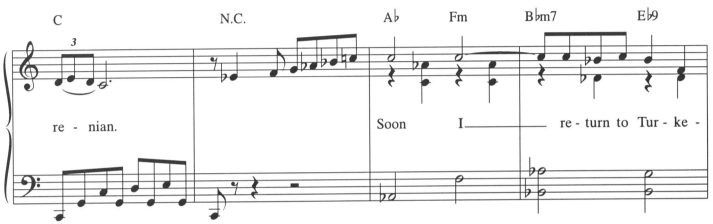

re - nian. Soon I_____ re-turn to Tur-ke-

stan;_____ I will_____ ask for her heart and

Chorus:

hand._____ Oh,_____ sweet Dar-da-nel-la,

ATF127

I Ain't Got Nobody
(And Nobody Cares for Me)

Words by
DAVID YOUNG
Music by
CHAS. WARFIELD

Copyright © 1997 by Carl Fischer, Inc.

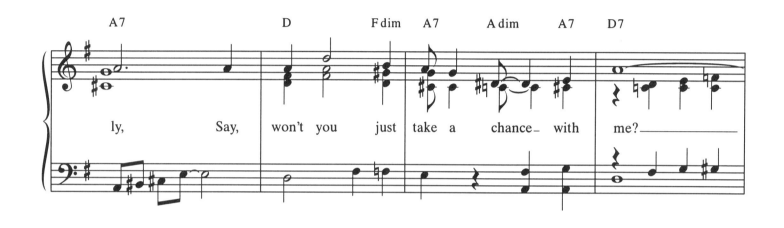

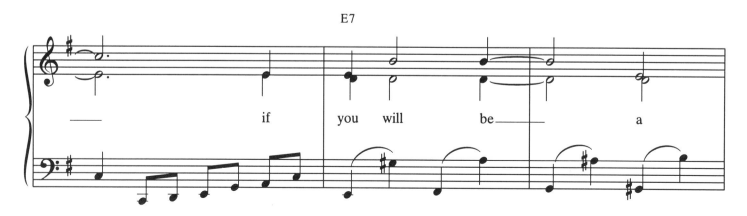

The Japanese Sandman

Words by
RAYMOND B. EGAN
Music by
RICHARD A. WHITING

ATF127

Sheik of Araby

Words by
HARRY SMITH and
FRANCIS WHEELER
Music by
TED SNYDER

Copyright © 1997 by Carl Fischer, Inc.

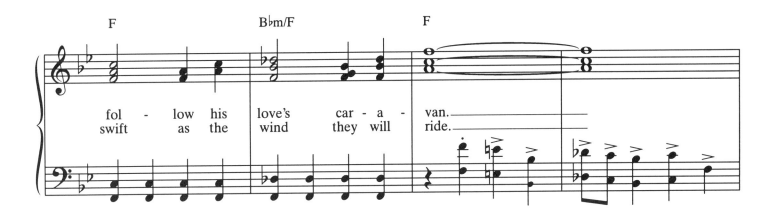

F   B♭m/F   F

fol - low his   love's   car - a - van._____
swift   as the   wind   they will   ride.

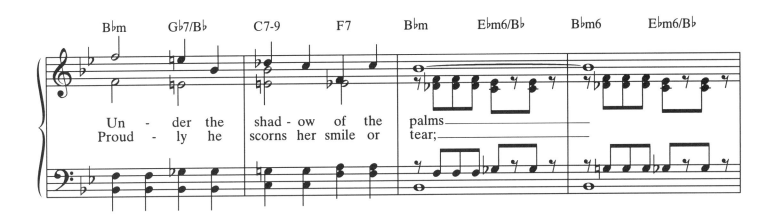

B♭m   G♭7/B♭   C7-9   F7   B♭m   E♭m6/B♭   B♭m6   E♭m6/B♭

Un - der the   shad - ow of the   palms_____
Proud - ly he   scorns her smile or   tear;_____

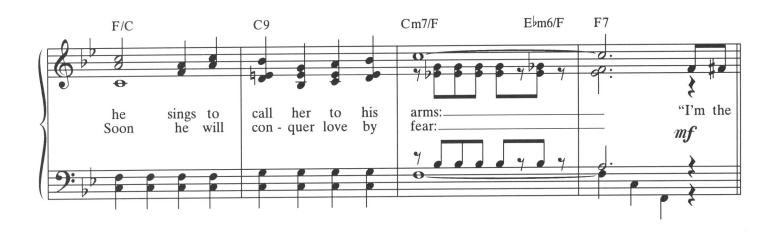

F/C   C9   Cm7/F   E♭m6/F   F7

he   sings to   call her to his   arms:_____ "I'm the
Soon   he will   con - quer love by   fear:_____

mf

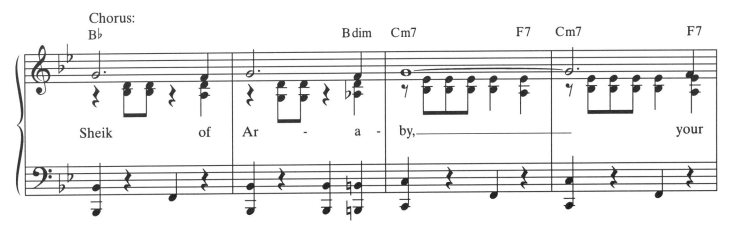

Chorus:
B♭   B dim   Cm7   F7   Cm7   F7

Sheik   of   Ar - a - by,_____ your

ATF127

love be-longs to me. At

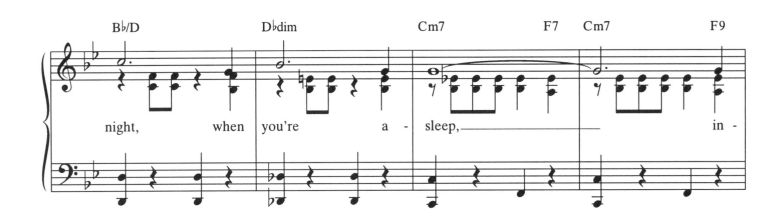

night, when you're a-sleep, in-

to your tent I'll creep. The

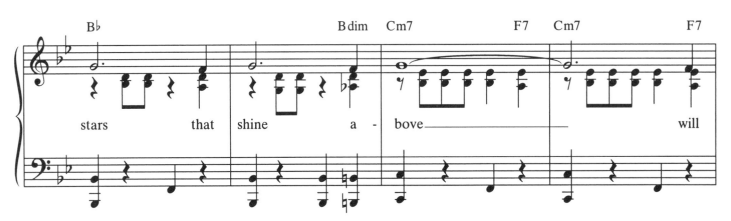

stars that shine a-bove will

light our way to love._____ You'll

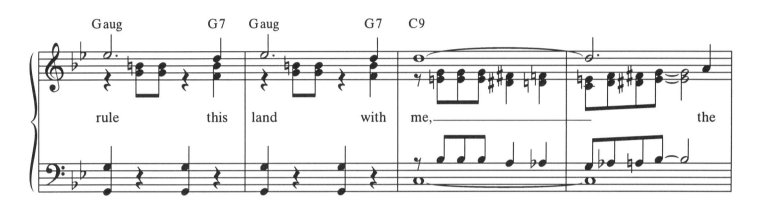

rule this land with me,_____ the

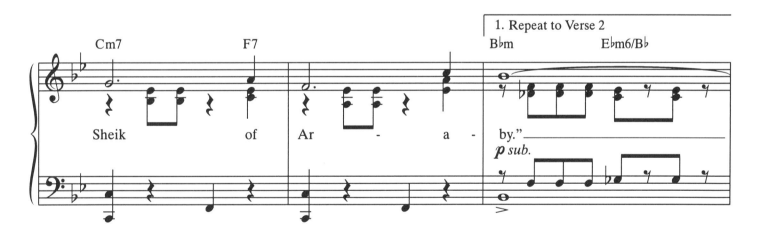

Sheik of Ar - a - by."_____
p sub.

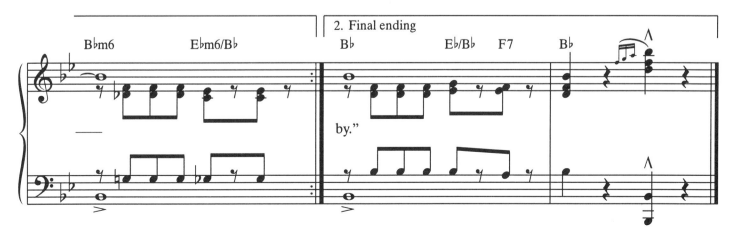

by."

Some of These Days

Words and Music by
SHELTON BROOKS

hon - ey,_____ you've had your way._____

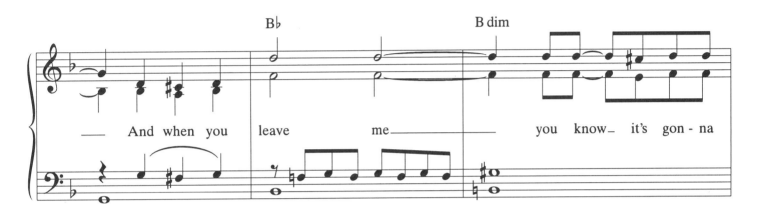

_____ And when you leave me_____ you know__ it's gon - na

grieve me._____ I'll miss__ my lit - tle dad - dad - dad - dy

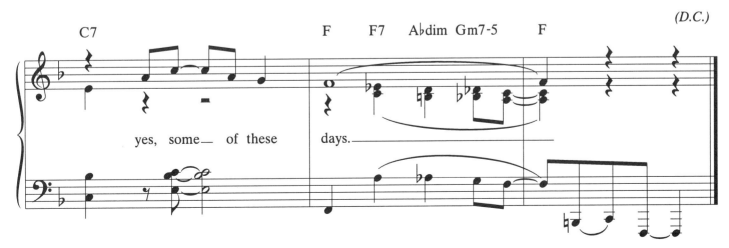

(D.C.)

yes, some__ of these days._____

ATF127

Somebody Stole My Gal

Words and Music by
LEO WOOD

Copyright © 1997 by Carl Fischer, Inc.

The Darktown Strutters' Ball

Words and Music by
SHELTON BROOKS

Moderately, with spirit

I've got some good news, hon - ey, an in - vit - a - tion to the
Well meet our high - toned neigh - bors, an ex - hi - bi - tion of the

Dark - town Ball.___ It's a ver - y swell___ af - fair, all the
"Ba - by Dolls,"___ And each one will do___ their best, just to

high - browns will be there.___ I'll wear my high silk hat and a
out - class all the rest.___ And there'll be danc - ers from ev - 'ry

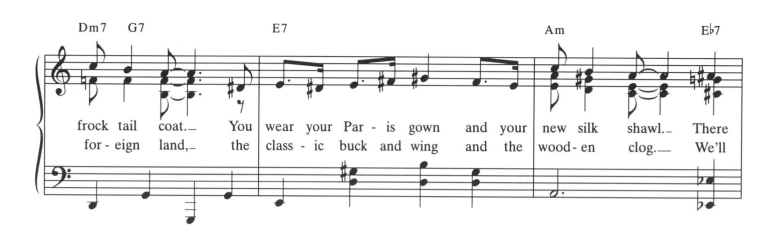

frock tail coat.— You wear your Par - is gown and your new silk shawl.— There
for - eign land,— the class - ic buck and wing and the wood - en clog.— We'll

ain't no doubt a - bout it, babe,— we'll be the best dressed in the ball.——
win that fif - ty dol - lar prize— when we step out and "Walk the Dog."—

Chorus

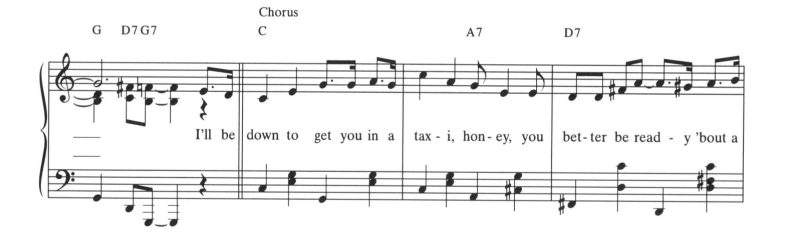

—— I'll be down to get you in a tax - i, hon - ey, you bet - ter be read - y 'bout a

half past eight.— Now, dear - ie, don't be late,— I want to

be there when the band starts play-in'. Re - mem-ber when we get there, hon-ey, the

two steps, I'm gon - na have 'em all.___ Gon - na dance out both my shoes___

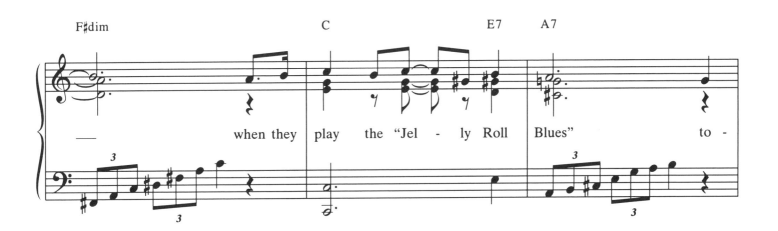

___ when they play the "Jel - ly Roll Blues" to -

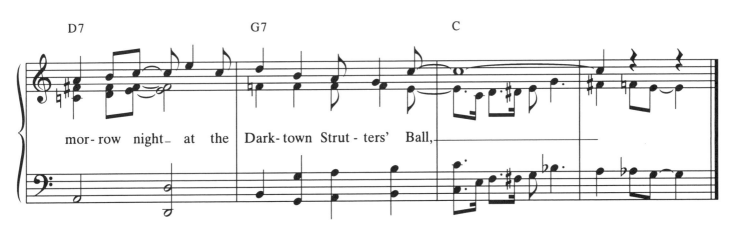

mor - row night___ at the Dark - town Strut - ters' Ball,_____

The St. Louis Blues

Words and Music by
W.C. HANDY

206

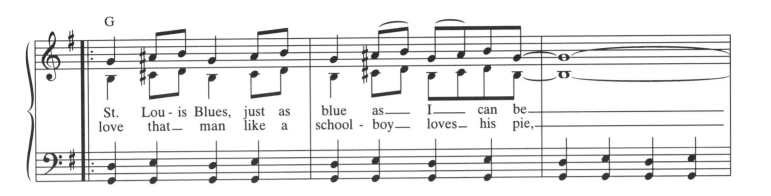

St. Lou - is Blues, just as   blue as   I   can be
love that   man   like a   school - boy   loves   his   pie,

That   man   got a heart like a   rock cast   in the   sea,
Like a   Ken - tuck - y Col' - nel   loves his   mint and   rye,

Or   else he   would - n't   gone   so   far   from   me.
I'll   love my   ba - by   till   the   day   I   die.

1. Repeat 3rd strain with 2nd lyric
G   G7   E dim   Cm6   G   C13   D♭13   D13

2. Final ending
G   G7   E dim   Cm6   G   A♭9   G9

I

Sugar Blues

Words by
LUCY FLETCHER
Music by
CLARENCE WILLIAMS

ATF127

Tishomingo Blues

By
SPENCER WILLIAMS

Copyright © 1997 by Carl Fischer, Inc.

There'll Be Some Changes Made

Words by
BILLY HIGGINS
Music by
W. BENTON OVERSTREET

Moderately slow, in four

Verse:

They say don't change the old for the new,___

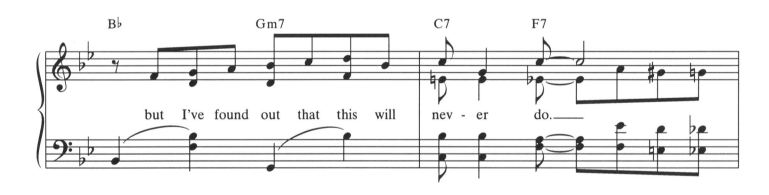

but I've found out that this will nev-er do.___

When you grow old, you don't last long;___

Brightly, in two

change in the weath - er, there's a change in the sea, and from now on there'll be a change in me._____ My walk will be dif - f'rent, my talk and my name;_____ Noth - in' a - bout____ me's gon - na be the same.____ I'm gon - na I'm gon - na change my way of liv - in' and if that ain't e - nough,____ change my long, tall Ma - ma for a lit - tle short fat, (Pa - pa)

Whispering

Words and Music by
JOHN SCHONBERGER,
RICHARD COBURN and VINCENT ROSE

Copyright © 1997 by Carl Fischer, Inc.

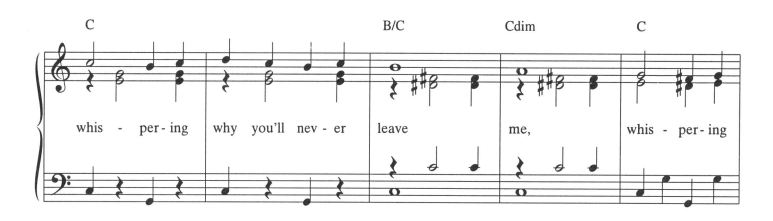

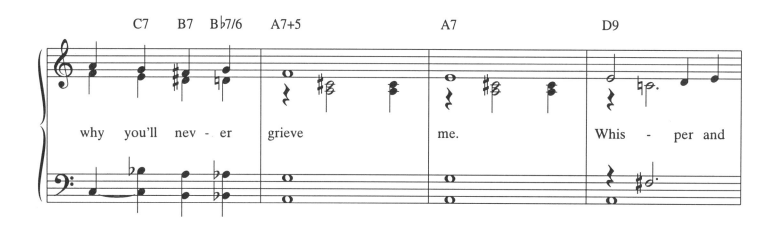

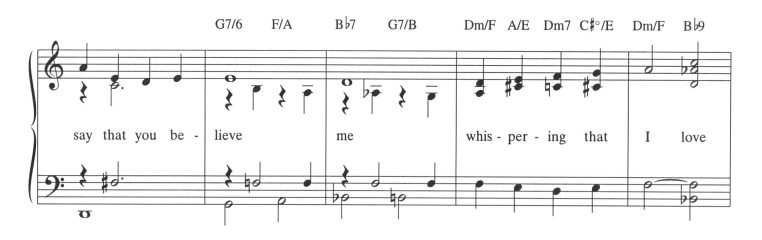

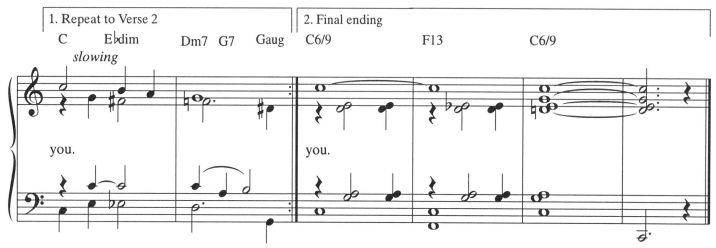

The World is Waiting for the Sunrise

Words by
EUGENE LOCKHART
Music by
ERNEST SEITZ

Slowly

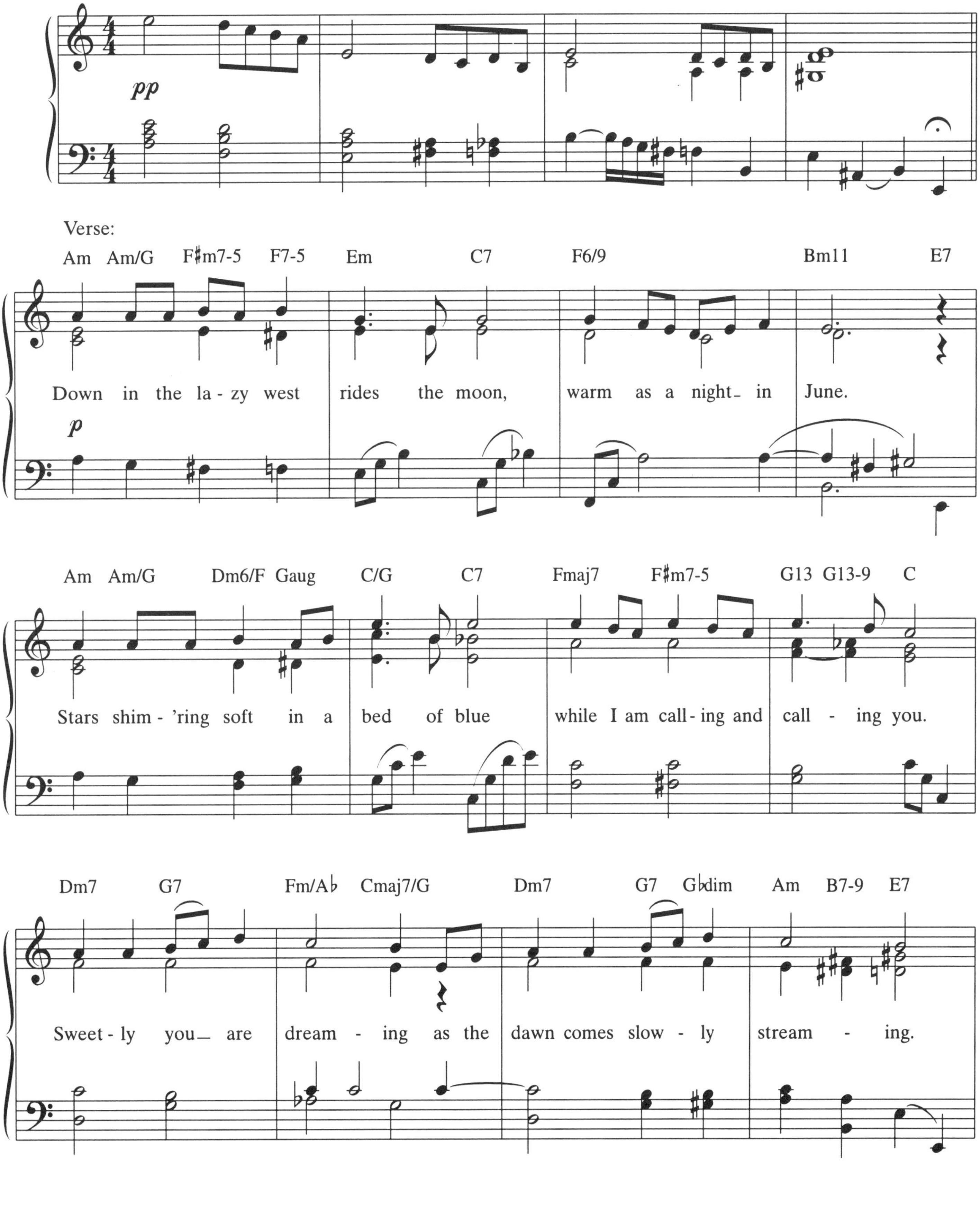

Moderate swing, in two

Chorus:

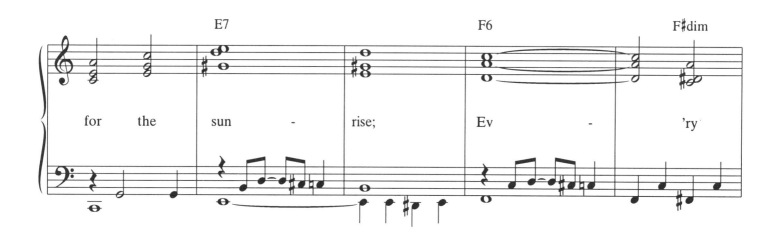

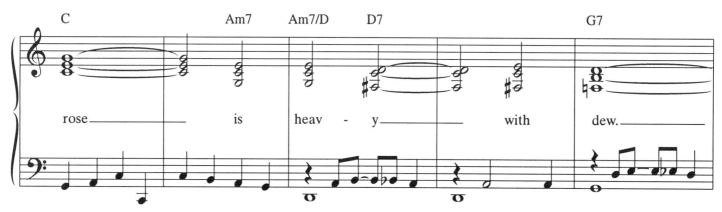

ATF127

For Our Troops in Uniform

Anchors Aweigh

Words by
Capt. ALFRED MILES, U. S. N. (Ret.)
Music by
Chas. A. ZIMMERMAN

Copyright © 1997 by Carl Fischer, Inc.

ATF127

The Caissons Go Rolling Along

By
EDMUND L. GRUBER

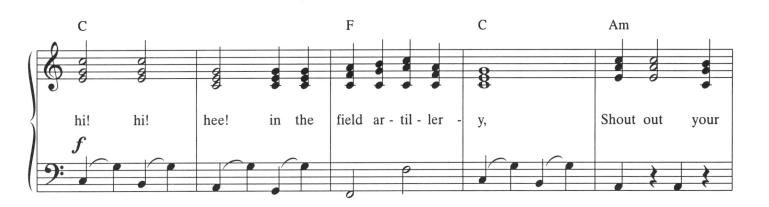

hi! hi! hee! in the field ar - til - ler - y, Shout out your

num - bers loud and strong,————————— for where - e'er you

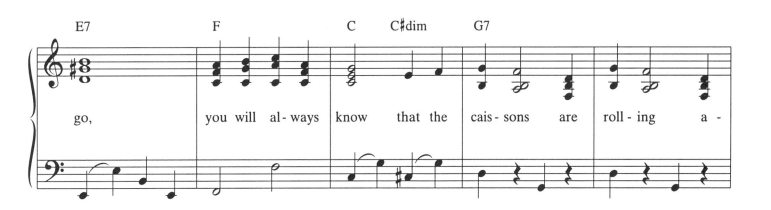

go, you will al - ways know that the cais - sons are roll - ing a -

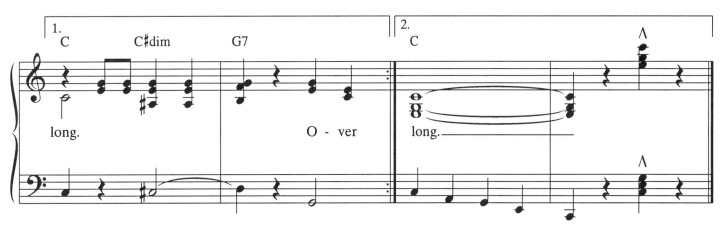

long. Over long.

ATF127

Over There

By
GEORGE M. COHAN

Spirited march tempo

Verse:

Johnny, get your gun, get your gun, get your gun.
Johnny, get your gun, get your gun, get your gun.

Take it on the run, on the run, on the run. Hear them
Johnny, show the Hun* you're a son of a gun. Hoist the

calling you and me, ev - 'ry son of
flag and let 'er fly, Yan - kee Doo - dle

*Hun = derogatory word for Germans in World War I.

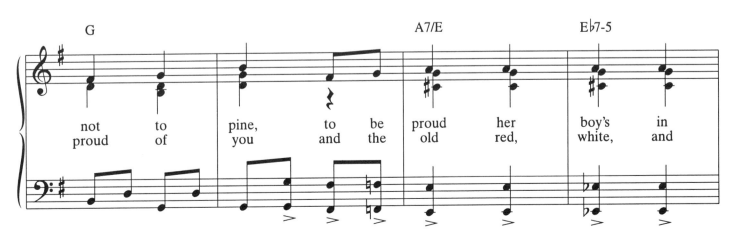

ATF127

ATF127

Pack Up Your Troubles in Your Old Kit-Bag
And Smile, Smile, Smile

Words by
GEORGE ASAF
Music by
FELIX POWELL

ATF127

Guide to World War I British slang; Lucifer = wooden match; fag = cigarette; Bosches = derogatory name for the Germans

ATF127

The U.S. Air Force
(The Wild Blue Yonder)

Words and Music by
ROBERT CRAWFORD

Off we go_____ in-to the wild blue yon - der,
Off we go_____ in-to the wild blue yon - der,

climb - ing high_____ in - to the sun._____
keep the wings_____ lev - el and true._____

Here they come,_____ zoom - ing to meet our thun - der,
If you'd live_____ to be a gray - haired won - der

The Marines' Hymn

Music adapted from
JACQUES OFFENBACH

Copyright © 1997 by Carl Fischer, Inc.

From the Turn of the Century

The Ace in the Hole

Words by
JAMES DEMPSEY
Music by
GEORGE MITCHELL

Moderately slow and rather freely

Verse:

Copyright © 1997 by Carl Fischer, Inc.

Moderately fast

Chorus

Some of them write to their old folks for coin, that's their old

mf

ace in the hole.____ Oth - ers have

"friends" in the old Ten - der - loin, that is their

ace in the hole.____ They tell you of
They tell you of

Bill Bailey, Won't You Please Come Home?

Words and Music by
HUGHIE CANNON

*B. and O. = Baltimore and Ohio Railroad

The Glow-Worm

Words by
LILLA CAYLEY ROBINSON
Music by
PAUL LINCKE

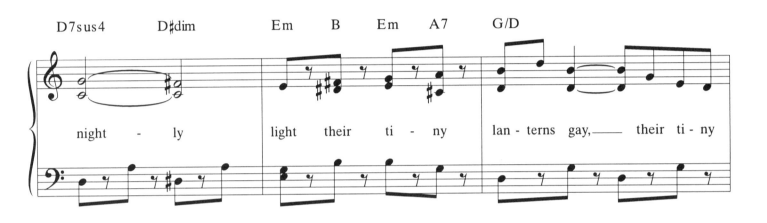

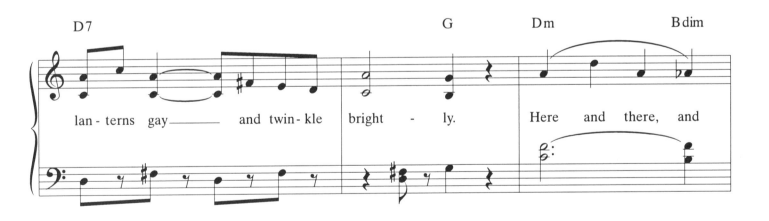

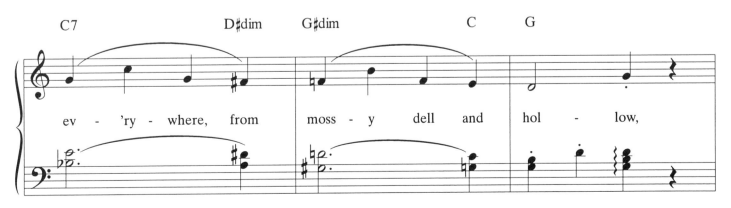

ATF127

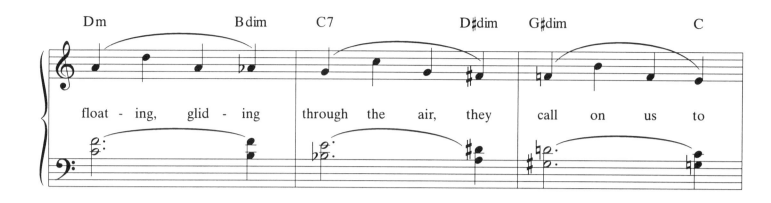

floating, gliding through the air, they call on us to

fol - low:

pp

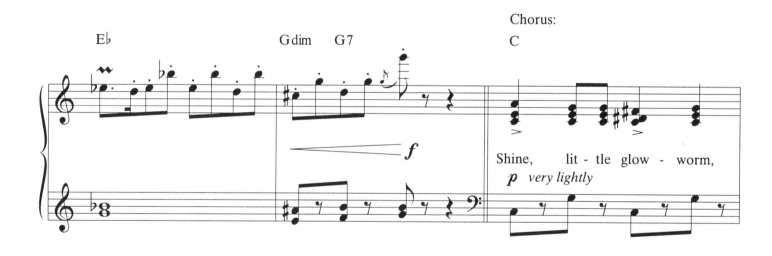

Chorus:

f

Shine, lit - tle glow - worm,
p very lightly

glim - mer, glim - mer, shine, lit - tle glow - worm, glim - mer, glim - mer.

I Want a Girl
(Just Like the Girl That Married Dear Old Dad)

Words by
WILLIAM DILLON
Music by
HARRY Von TILZER

Moderately, like a march

ff

Verse:

When I was a boy my moth-er of-ten said to me, "Get
By the old mill stream there sits a cou-ple old and gray. Though

mf

mar-ried, boy, and see how hap-py you will be."
years have rolled a-way, how their hearts are young to-day.

I have looked all o-ver but no girl-ie can I find
Moth-er dear looks up at Dad with love light in her eye;

who
He

259

ATF127

260

ATF127

A Bicycle Built for Two
(Daisy Bell)

Words and Music by
HARRY DACRE

Waltz tempo
Verse

There is a flow-er with-in my heart, Dai - sy,

Dai - sy. Plant-ed one day by a glanc-ing dart,

plant-ed by Dai - sy Bell! Wheth-er she loves me or

loves me not, some-times it's hard to tell.

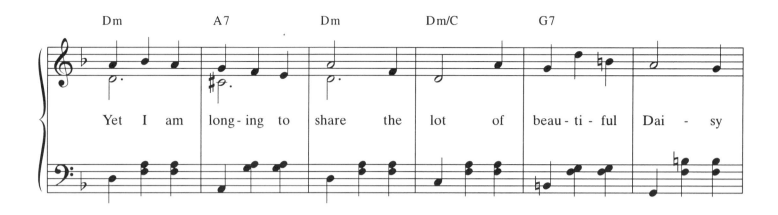

Yet I am long-ing to share the lot of beau-ti-ful Dai - sy

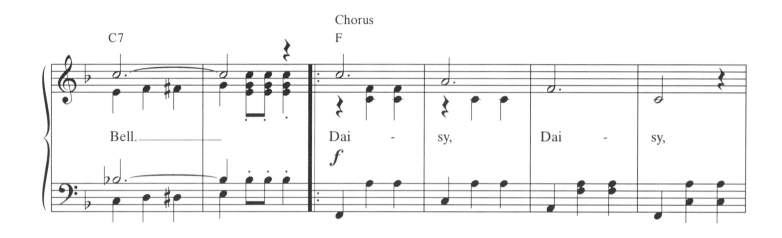

Chorus

Bell._____ Dai - sy, Dai - sy,

give me your an - swer, do._____ I'm half

cra - zy all for the love of you._____ It

Meet Me in St. Louis, Louis

Words by
ANDREW B. STERLING
Music by
KERRY MILLS

Moderate, spirited waltz

Now
The

Verse:
C

Lou - is came home to the flat,_____ he
dress - es that hung in the hall_____ were

Dm   G7

hung up his coat and his hat._____ He
gone; She had tak - en them all._____ She

C   F♯dim   C   E♭7-5

gazed all a - round, but no wife - y he found, so he
took all his rings and the rest of his things, the

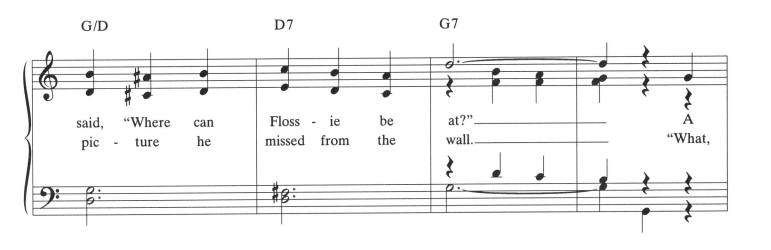

said, "Where can Floss - ie be at?"_____ A
pic - ture he missed from the wall._____ "What,

note on the ta - ble he spied,_____ he
mov - ing?" the jan - it - or said,_____ "Your

read it just once, then he cried._____ It
rent is paid three months a - head!"_____ "What

ran, "Lou - is, dear, it's too slow for me here, so I
good is the flat?" said poor Lou - is, "Read that." And the

ATF127

The Sidewalks of New York
(East Side, West Side)

Words and Music by
CHAS. B. LAWLOR and
JAMES W. BLAKE

Verse:

1. Down in front of Ca-sey's old brown wood-en stoop, on a sum-mer's eve-ning we
2. That's where John-ny Ca-sey and lit-tle Jim-my Crowe with Ja-key Krause, the ba-ker, who
3. Things have changed since those times some are up in "G." Oth-ers, they are wand-'rers, but they

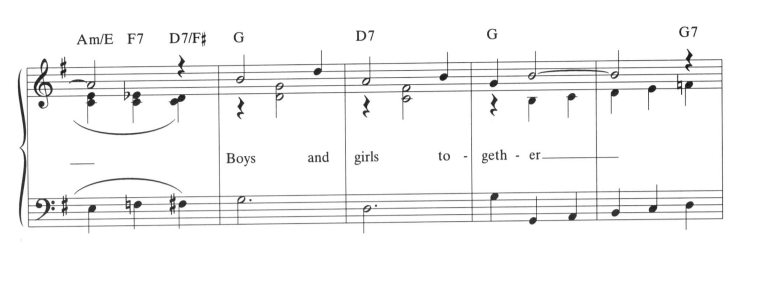

Boys and girls to - geth - er

me and Ma - mie Rorke,

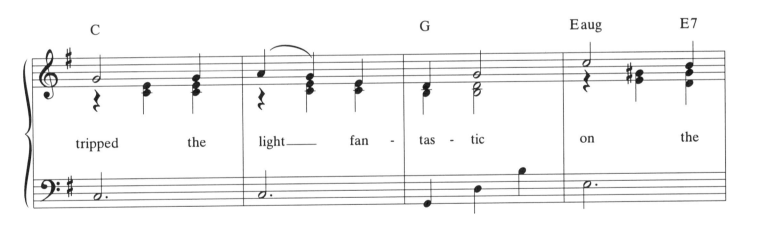

tripped the light fan - tas - tic on the

(D.C.)

side - walks of New York.

ATF127

Just For Fun
Songs & Piano Solos

Ain't We Got Fun

Words by
GUS KAHN
and RAYMOND B. EGAN
Music by
RICHARD A. WHITING

Dagger Dance
(From the opera "Natoma")

Words and Music by
VICTOR HERBERT

Ja-Da

Words and Music by
BOB CARLETON

Copyright © 1997 by Carl Fischer, Inc.

Johnson Rag

By
GUY HALL

ATF127

K-K-K-Katy

Words and Music by
GEOFFREY O'HARA

Moderately, with a lilt

Listen to the Mockingbird

Words by
ALICE HAWTHORNE
(SEPTIMUS WINNER)
Music by
RICHARD MILBURN

12th Street Rag

By
EUDAY L. BOWMAN

Moderate ragtime tempo

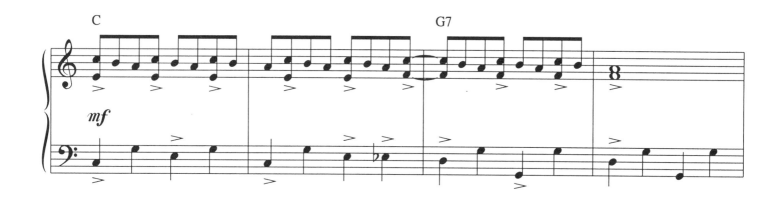

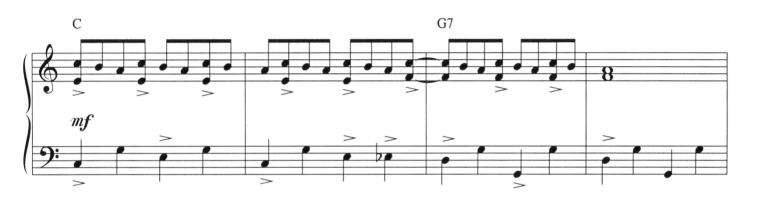

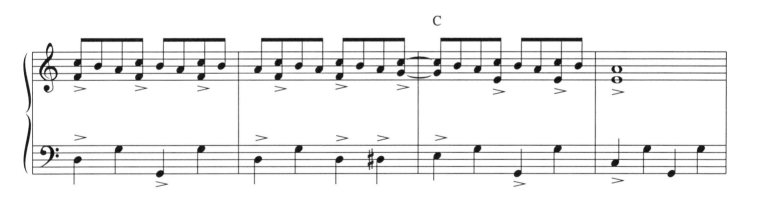

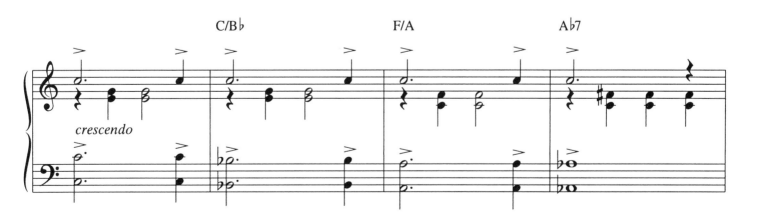

ATF127

Waltzing Matilda

Words by
A.B. "BANJO" PATERSON
Music by
MARIE COWAN

youʼll come a-waltz-ing Ma - til - da with me. And he sang as he watched and

mf

wait-ed till his bil-ly boiled, "Youʼll come a-waltz-ing Ma - til - da with me!"

Additional Words

2. Down came a jumbuck to drink at the billabong,
   Up jumped the swagman and grabbed him with glee.
   And he sang as he stowed that jumbuck in his tucker bag,
   "Youʼll come a-waltzing Matilda with me!"
   "Waltzing Matilda, waltzing Matilda
   Youʼll come a-waltzing Matilda with me!"
   And he sang as he stowed that jumbuck in his tucker bag,
   "Youʼll come a-waltzing Matilda with me!"

3. Up rode the squatter, mounted on his throughbred,
   Down came the troopers, one, two, three.
   "Whereʼs that jolly jumbuck youʼve got in your tucker bag?"
   "Youʼll come a-waltzing Matilda with me!"
   "Waltzing Matilda, waltzing Matilda,
   Youʼll come a-waltzing Matilda with me!"
   "Whereʼs that jolly jumbuck youʼve got in your tucker bag?"
   "Youʼll come a-waltzing Matilda with me!"

4. Up jumped the swagman, sprang into the billabong,
   "Youʼll never catch me alive!" said he.
   And his ghost may be heard as you pass by that billabong,
   "Youʼll come a-waltzing Matilda with me!"
   "Waltzing Matilda, waltzing Matilda,
   Youʼll come a-waltzing Matilda with me!"
   And his ghost may be heard as you pass by that billabong,
   "Youʼll come a-waltzing Matilda with me!"

Guide to Australian slang: swag = a bundle wrapped in a blanket; swagman = hobo; billabong = waterhole in a dried up river bed; coolibah tree = eucalyptus tree; billy = a tin can used as a kettle; jumbuck=sheep; tucker bag = a bag for carrying food; waltzing Matilda = bumming around; squatter = a large scale sheep farmer

The Whistler and His Dog

By
ARTHUR PRYOR*

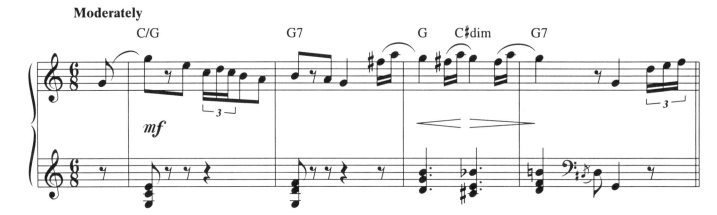

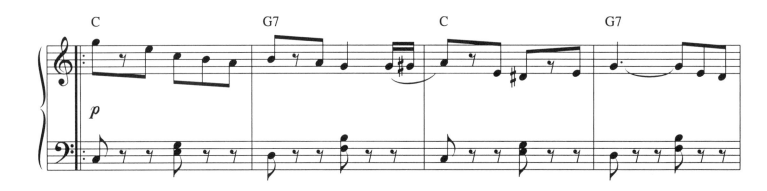

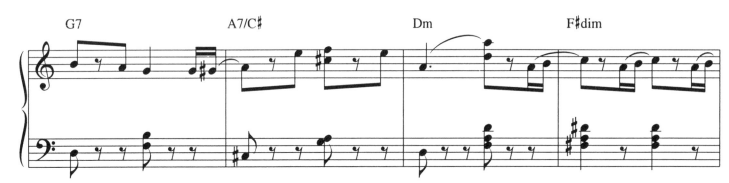

*This arrangement based on Maxwell Eckstein's piano adaptation

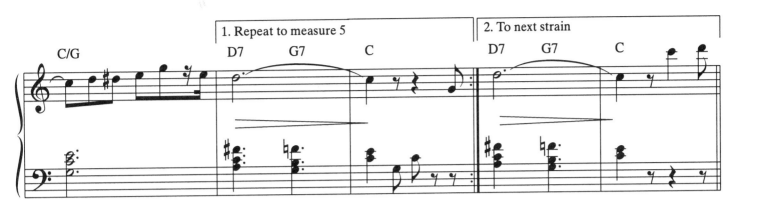

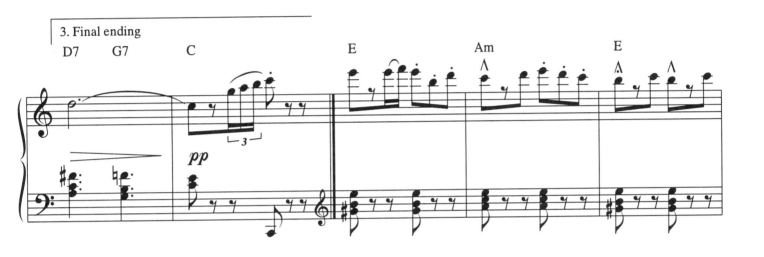

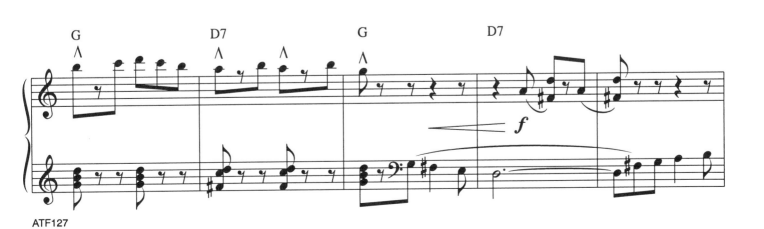

ATF127

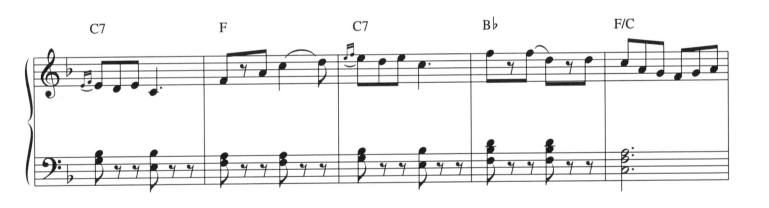

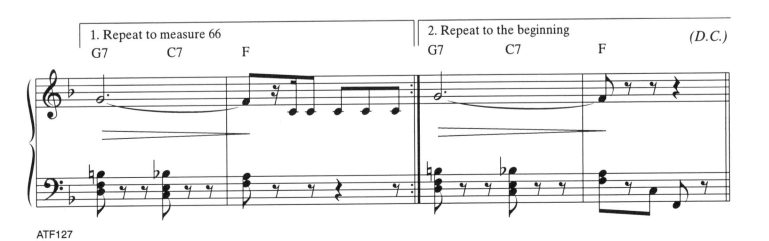

ATF127

Oh, Johnny, Oh, Johnny, Oh!

Words by
ED ROSE
Music by
ABE OLMAN

Copyright © 1997 by Carl Fischer, Inc.

A Pretty Girl Is Like a Melody

Margie
Oh, You Beautiful Doll
Paper Doll
Pretty Baby
A Pretty Girl is Like a Melody

A Pretty Girl Is Like A Melody

Words and Music by
IRVING BERLIN

Copyright © 1997 by Carl Fischer, Inc.

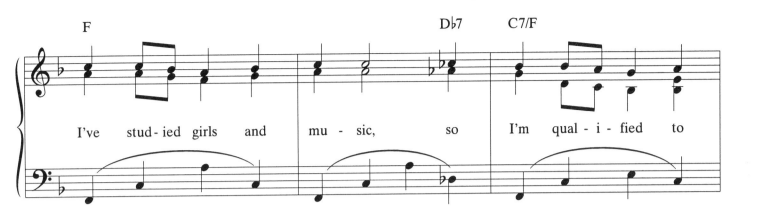

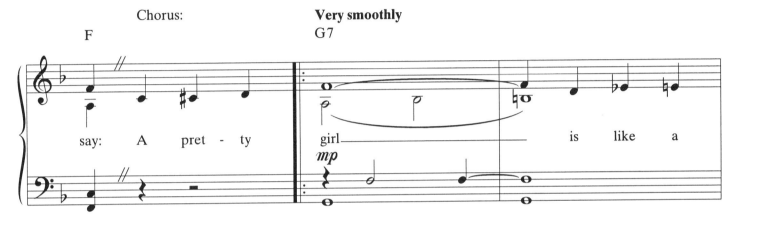

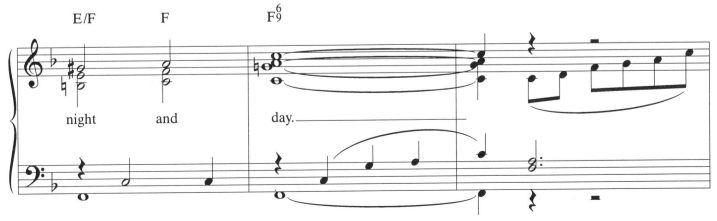

ATF127

306

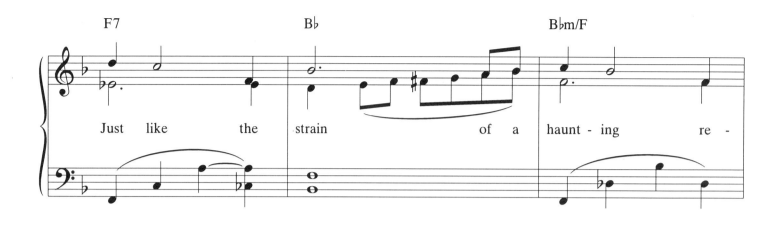

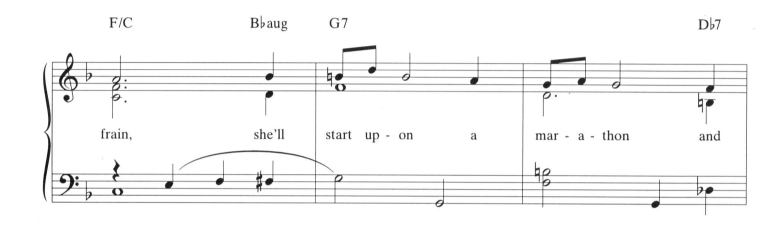

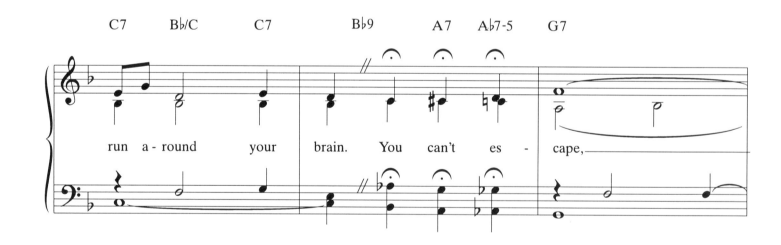

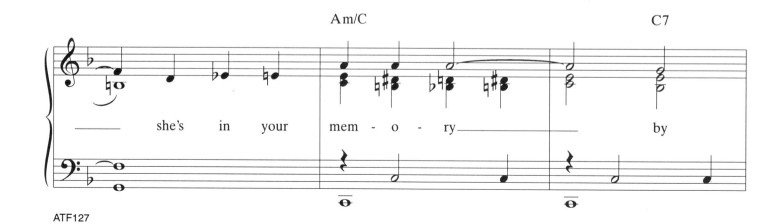

Margie

Words by
BENNY DAVIS
Music by
CON CONRAD and
J. RUSSEL ROBINSON

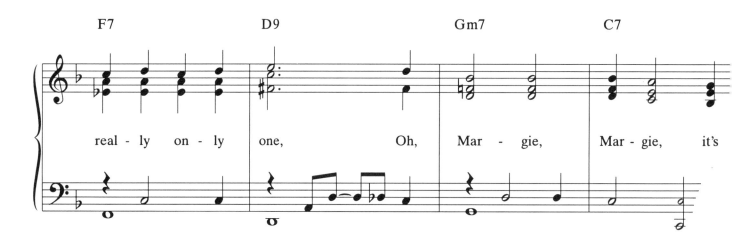

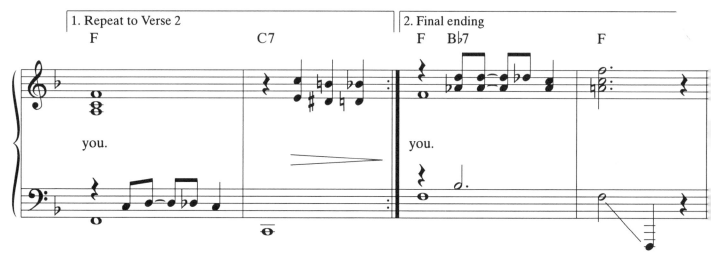

Paper Doll

Words and Music by
JOHNNY S. BLACK

Copyright © 1997 by Carl Fischer, Inc.

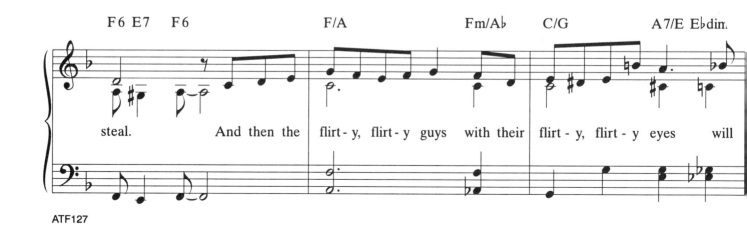

Oh, You Beautiful Doll

Words by
A. SEYMOUR BROWN
Music by
NAT D. AYER

The Great Irish Songbook

Arranged & Edited by Dan Fox

With a special section of traditional Irish jigs, reels and hornpipes

This is the finest vocal collection of Irish favorites ever assembled in one book.

The over eighty songs are expertly and easily arranged by Dan Fox for piano with guitar chords.

This edition includes an essay on Celtic and Irish music, arrangements categorized by section and top, an index of songs listed by the first lines and a special section of jigs, reels and hornpipes.

The Great Italian Songbook

This is a superb vocal collection of Italian music assembled in one book.

From Classic and Neapolitan songs to Operatic Arias and Italian-American Hits, these 38 songs are expertly and easily arranged by Dan Fox for voice and piano with guitar chords.

This edition includes an essay surveying the history and development of Italian song, arrangements categorized by section and topic, and an index of songs listed by the first lines.

Arranged & Edited by Dan Fox